D1095417

INTERMEDIATE
REAL ANALYSIS

INTERMEDIATE REAL ANALYSIS

Maynard J. Mansfield
Purdue University
at Fort Wayne

PRINDLE, WEBER & SCHMIDT, INCORPORATED
Boston   London   Sydney

Preface

This book is intended to prepare the student for a rigorous course in either advanced calculus or introductory theory of functions of a real variable. It also is meant to provide the prospective or practicing secondary school teacher with enough theoretical background to do a creditable job of teaching an introductory calculus course. It is assumed that all students using the book will have had at least a one-year, college-level course in calculus.

The development in Chapter 1 of the system of real numbers begins with the Peano postulates and concludes with the complete-ordered-field property. The individual instructor may choose to include as little or as much of this material as he desires, since the remainder of the book depends only on the complete-ordered-field property. Many instructors will probably want to use the rational number field as a point of departure; this can be done without difficulty by regarding Theorem 61 as axiomatic. Other possible points of departure are provided by Theorem 46 and by Theorems 95, 96, 97, and 101. Incidentally, the development of the system of natural numbers given here is a variation on Landau's classic theme, *Grundlagen der Analysis*, while the treatment of real numbers as cuts follows in general outline that given by McCoy in the first edition of his *Introduction to Modern Algebra*.

Although the text itself does not include a recital of the basic concepts of abstract algebra and informal set theory, these concepts and some of their implications are discussed in the Appendix. The Appendix is coordinated with the rest of the text by means of marginal references. Thus, for example, when the word "group" appears for the first time (on page 17) it is printed in italics, and the notation A_1 appears in the margin. This means that the definition of a group will be found in section A_1 of the Appendix.

Strict adherence to the principles of logic requires that "if and only if" be used in formulating proper definitions. Many authors, however, favor the use of "if" alone, apparently on the grounds that "only if" is implied by the act of defining. It seems, therefore, that Halmos' "iff" offers a reasonable compromise for use in definitions, and this convention is employed throughout the book.

Exercises containing results needed later in the text are signalized by ▷, and the end of each proof is indicated by □.

Maynard J. Mansfield
Fort Wayne, Indiana

Contents

≡ THE DERIVATIVE

≥ THE RIEMANN THEORY OF INTEGRATION

> INFINITE SERIES

APPENDIX

References

Index

INTERMEDIATE
REAL ANALYSIS

THE REAL
NUMBERS

A rigorous development of the theory of real analysis requires a considerable knowledge of the structure of that sophisticated mathematical
object known as the system of real numbers. The story of the development of this system began before man learned to read and write, but it
did not reach a definitive climax until 1872, when Richard Dedekind,
a German mathematician, published *Continuity and Irrational Numbers*.
The subject matter of this first chapter is, therefore, the distillate of
centuries of mathematical thought.

The Natural Numbers

We shall begin our development of the system of real numbers in
an historically appropriate manner by considering those familiar

1

numbers which we employ in counting, the natural numbers. We shall not attempt to define natural numbers, but rather, following the Italian mathematician Giuseppe Peano (1858–1932), we shall accept "natural number" as an undefined, or primitive, term. This does not mean that we shall allow ourselves all manner of liberty in dealing with natural numbers. On the contrary, we shall state, in the form of axioms, certain properties of the natural numbers, and these are the only properties which we shall permit ourselves to use.

S_1 Specifically, we assume that there exists a *set* **N** of objects called *natural numbers* satisfying the following axioms:

Axiom 1. The set **N** is not empty.

S_{16} *Axiom* 2. There exists a *one-to-one mapping s* of **N** onto a *proper subset*
S_3 of **N**.

S_3 *Axiom* 3. If M is a *subset* of **N**, and if M has the following two properties:
[1] $x \in M$ implies $s(x) \in M$, and
[2] there is a $y \in M$ such that $y \neq s(x)$ for every $x \in$ **N**,
then $M =$ **N**.

In the work that follows, we shall refer to the mapping s whose existence is postulated in Axiom 2 as the *successor mapping*. Furthermore, for each $x \in$ **N** we shall refer to the natural number $s(x)$ as the *successor* of x.

1   THEOREM

For every $x \in$ **N** and for every $y \in$ **N**, $s(x) = s(y)$ if and only if $x = y$.

Proof

If $x = y$, then $s(x) = s(y)$ because, by Axiom 2, s is a mapping. If $s(x) = s(y)$, then $x = y$ because, by Axiom 2, s is one-to-one.   □

2   THEOREM

There exists a unique $y \in$ **N** such that $y \neq s(x)$ for every $x \in$ **N**.

Proof

It follows from Axiom 2 that there is at least one such y (s maps onto a *proper* subset of **N**). Assume that there are two distinct natural numbers y and $y^\bullet$ such that $y \neq s(x)$ for all $x \in$ **N** and $y^\bullet \neq s(x)$ for all $x \in$ **N**. Let

$$M = \{x \in \mathbf{N} : x \neq y^\bullet\}.$$

If $x \in M$, then $x \in \mathbf{N}$, so $s(x) \neq y^{\bullet}$. Hence $s(x) \in M$. Therefore $x \in M$ implies $s(x) \in M$.

Furthermore $y \neq y^{\bullet}$ by hypothesis, so $y \in M$.

Since $y \neq s(x)$ for every $x \in \mathbf{N}$, it follows from Axiom 3 that $M = \mathbf{N}$. But $M \neq \mathbf{N}$, because $y^{\bullet} \in \mathbf{N}$ but $y^{\bullet} \notin M$.

Hence there is at most one such y, hence exactly one. □

3 DEFINITION

The unique natural number y, having the property that $y \neq s(x)$ for every $x \in \mathbf{N}$, will be called *one* and will be denoted by the symbol 1.

4 THEOREM

If $y \in \mathbf{N}$ and $y \neq 1$, then there exists a unique $x \in \mathbf{N}$ such that $y = s(x)$.

Proof

If $y \neq s(x)$ for every $x \in \mathbf{N}$, then, according to Definition 3, $y = 1$. The uniqueness of x for a given $y \neq 1$ follows from Theorem 1. □

The next theorem provides us with our most important tool for analyzing the set of natural numbers. The reader will observe that it is a restatement of Axiom 3 using the terminology of Definition 3.

5 THEOREM   Principle of Finite Induction

If M is a subset of $\mathbf{N}$ that has the following two properties:

[1] $x \in M$ implies $s(x) \in M$, and
[2] $1 \in M$,

then $M = \mathbf{N}$.

EXERCISES

1   ▷ Use the principle of finite induction to prove that

$$x \neq s(x) \qquad \text{for every} \quad x \in \mathbf{N}.$$

2   Give an example of a system that satisfies Axioms 1 and 3, but

▷ Exercise items marked in this way contain results that are needed in the sequel.

that fails to satisfy Axiom 2 because the mapping s is not one-to-one.

3   Give an example of a system that satisfies Axioms 1 and 2 but not Axiom 3.

Addition of Natural Numbers

S_{18} There are infinitely many *binary operations* on the set **N**. Our present task is to apply the rather limited machinery we have available to the problem of singling out a particular one of these operations to be given the name "addition." Since the only structure that has been introduced into **N** is the successor mapping s, we must characterize the addition operation in terms of s.

6   THEOREM

There exists exactly one binary operation $+$ on **N** such that

$$x + 1 = s(x) \qquad \text{for every} \quad x \in \mathbf{N},$$

and

$$x + s(y) = s(x + y) \qquad \text{for every} \quad x \in \mathbf{N}, y \in \mathbf{N}.$$

Proof

We shall show first that there exists *at most* one such binary operation. Assume that $*$ is a binary operation on **N** such that

$$x * 1 = s(x) \qquad \text{for every} \quad x \in \mathbf{N},$$

and

$$x * s(y) = s(x * y) \qquad \text{for every} \quad x \in \mathbf{N}, y \in \mathbf{N}.$$

L_2 For *fixed but arbitrary* $x \in \mathbf{N}$ let

$$M_x = \{ y \in \mathbf{N} : x + y = x * y \}.$$

L_1 *Assume that* $y \in M_x$. Then $x + y = x * y$. Hence

$$x + s(y) = s(x + y) = s(x * y) = x * s(y),$$

and so $s(y) \in M_x$. Therefore $y \in M_x$ implies $s(y) \in M_x$. Also, $x + 1 = s(x) = x * 1$, so $1 \in M_x$.

Therefore, by the principle of finite induction, $M_x = \mathbf{N}$ for every

$x \in \mathbf{N}$. That is, $x + y = x * y$ for every $x \in \mathbf{N}$ and every $y \in \mathbf{N}$. Hence there is at most one such operation on $\mathbf{N}$.

Now we shall show that there is *at least* one such operation on $\mathbf{N}$. Let M be the set of all natural numbers x for which there exists a mapping f_x of $\mathbf{N}$ into itself such that

$$f_x(1) = s(x),$$

and

$$f_x(s(y)) = s(f_x(y)) \qquad \text{for every} \quad y \in \mathbf{N}.$$

Assume that $x \in M$. Then a mapping f_x having the above properties exists. Let.

$$g(u) = s(f_x(u)) \qquad \text{for every} \quad u \in \mathbf{N}.$$

Then

$$g(1) = s(f_x(1)) = s(s(x)),$$

and

$$g(s(y)) = s(f_x(s(y))) = s(s(f_x(y))) = s(g(y)) \qquad \text{for every} \quad y \in \mathbf{N}.$$

Therefore g has the properties required of $f_{s(x)}$, and therefore $f_{s(x)}$ exists. Therefore $s(x) \in M$. Hence $x \in M$ implies that $s(x) \in M$.

Let $h(u) = s(u)$ for every $u \in \mathbf{N}$. Then

$$h(1) = s(1),$$

and

$$h(s(y)) = s(s(y)) = s(h(y)) \qquad \text{for every} \quad y \in \mathbf{N}.$$

Therefore h has the properties required of f_1, and so f_1 exists. Hence $1 \in M$.

Therefore, by the principle of finite induction, $M = \mathbf{N}$. That is, such a mapping f_x exists for every $x \in \mathbf{N}$.

For each $x \in \mathbf{N}$ and each $y \in \mathbf{N}$, let

$$x + y = f_x(y).$$

Then

$$x + 1 = f_x(1) = s(x) \qquad \text{for every} \quad x \in \mathbf{N},$$

and

$$x + s(y) = f_x(s(y)) = s(f_x(y)) = s(x + y) \qquad \text{for every} \quad x \in \mathbf{N}, y \in \mathbf{N}.$$

Therefore there is at least one such binary operation on $\mathbf{N}$, and hence exactly one. □

7   DEFINITION

The unique binary operation $+$ on $\mathbf{N}$ whose existence is guaranteed by Theorem 6 will be called *addition*. For each $x \in \mathbf{N}$ and each $y \in \mathbf{N}$ the natural number $x + y$ will be called the *sum* of x and y.

8   COROLLARY

Addition has the following properties:

[1] $1 + y = s(y)$ for every $y \in \mathbf{N}$, and
[2] $s(x) + y = s(x + y)$ for every $x \in \mathbf{N}$ and every $y \in \mathbf{N}$.

Proof

In the second (at-least-one) part of the proof of Theorem 6 we showed that $x + y = f_x(y)$, where $f_1(u) = s(u)$ for every $u \in \mathbf{N}$ and $f_{s(x)}(u) = s(f_x(u))$ for every $u \in \mathbf{N}$. Therefore

$$1 + y = f_1(y) = s(y) \qquad \text{for every} \quad y \in \mathbf{N},$$

and

$$s(x) + y = f_{s(x)}(y) = s(f_x(y)) = s(x + y) \qquad \text{for every} \quad x \in \mathbf{N},\, y \in \mathbf{N}. \quad □$$

We now proceed to establish the fundamental properties of addition. While the theorems are not exactly of overwhelming novelty, they do form an important part of the development.

9   THEOREM   Commutative Law of Addition

For every $x \in \mathbf{N}$ and every $y \in \mathbf{N}$,

$$x + y = y + x.$$

Proof

For fixed but arbitrary $y \in \mathbf{N}$, let

$$M_y = \{x \in N : x + y = y + x\}.$$

Assume that $x \in M_y$. Then $x + y = y + x$. Hence

$$s(x) + y = s(x + y) \qquad \text{C8 (i.e., by Corollary 8)}$$

$$= s(y + x) \qquad \text{T1}$$

$$= y + s(x) \qquad \text{T6}$$

and so $s(x) \in M_y$. Therefore $x \in M_y$ implies $s(x) \in M_y$.

Moreover, $\qquad\qquad\qquad 1 + y = s(y) \qquad \text{C8}$

$$= y + 1 \qquad \text{T6}$$

and so $1 \in M_y$.

Therefore $M_y = \mathbf{N}$ for every $y \in \mathbf{N}$.

10   THEOREM   Associative Law of Addition

For every $x \in \mathbf{N}$, every $y \in \mathbf{N}$, and every $z \in \mathbf{N}$,

$$(x + y) + z = x + (y + z).$$

Proof

For fixed but arbitrary x and y in $\mathbf{N}$, let

$$M_{xy} = \{z \in N : (x + y) + z = x + (y + z)\}.$$

Assume that $z \in M_{xy}$. Then $(x + y) + z = x + (y + z)$. Hence

$$(x + y) + s(z) = s((x + y) + z) \qquad \text{T6}$$

$$= s(x + (y + z)) \qquad \text{T1}$$

$$= x + s(y + z) \qquad \text{T6}$$

$$= x + (y + s(z)) \qquad \text{T6}$$

and so $s(z) \in M_{xy}$. Therefore $z \in M_{xy}$ implies that $s(z) \in M_{xy}$.

Now

$$(x + y) + 1 = s(x + y) \qquad \text{T6}$$

$$= x + s(y) \qquad \text{T6}$$

$$= x + (y + 1) \qquad \text{T6}$$

and so $1 \in M_{xy}$.

Therefore $M_{xy} = N$ for every $x \in \mathbf{N}$ and every $y \in \mathbf{N}$. □

11   THEOREM   Additive Cancellation Law

If x, y, and z are natural numbers such that

$$x + y = x + z$$

then
$$y = z.$$

Proof

Assume that y and z are natural numbers such that $y \neq z$. We shall prove that $x + y \neq x + z$ for every $x \in N$.

Let $M = \{x \in \mathbf{N} : x + y \neq x + z\}$.

Assume that $x \in M$. Then $x + y \neq x + z$. Hence, by Theorem 1, $s(x + y) \neq s(x + z)$. But according to Corollary 8, $s(x + y) = s(x) + y$ and $s(x + z) = s(x) + z$. Therefore $s(x) + y \neq s(x) + z$, and so $s(x) \in M$. Hence $x \in M$ implies $s(x) \in M$.

Also by Corollary 8, $1 + y = s(y)$ and $1 + z = s(z)$. Since $y \neq z$, it follows from Theorem 1 that $s(y) \neq s(z)$. Hence $1 + y \neq 1 + z$, and so $1 \in M$.

Therefore $M = \mathbf{N}$. That is, if $y \neq z$, then $x + y \neq x + z$ for every $x \in N$. Therefore if $x + y = x + z$ for some $x \in \mathbf{N}$, then $y = z$. $\square$

EXERCISES

1   Let the symbols 2 and 4 denote the natural numbers $s(1)$ and $s(s(s(1)))$, respectively. Prove that $2 + 2 = 4$.

2   Prove that for all natural numbers $w, x, y,$ and z,

$$(((w + x) + y) + z) = (w + x) + (y + z) = w + ((x + y) + z)$$
$$= w + (x + (y + z)) = (w + (x + y)) + z.$$

3   ▷ Prove that for every $x \in \mathbf{N}$ and every $u \in \mathbf{N}$,

$$x + u \neq x.$$

Multiplication of Natural Numbers

Here again we are faced with the problem of singling out a particular one of the infinitely many binary operations on **N**.

12   THEOREM

There exists exactly one binary operation $\cdot$ on **N** such that

$$x \cdot 1 = x \qquad \text{for every} \quad x \in \mathbf{N},$$
and
$$x \cdot s(y) = x \cdot y + x \qquad \text{for every} \quad x \in \mathbf{N}, y \in \mathbf{N}.$$

Proof

First we shall show that there is *at most* one such operation on **N**. Assume that $*$ is a binary operation on **N** such that

$$x * 1 = x \qquad \text{for every} \quad x \in \textbf{N},$$

and

$$x * s(y) = x * y + x \qquad \text{for every} \quad x \in \textbf{N}, y \in \textbf{N}.$$

For fixed but arbitrary $x \in \textbf{N}$, let

$$M_x = \{y \in \textbf{N} : x \cdot y = x * y\}.$$

Assume that $y \in M_x$. Then $x \cdot y = x * y$. Hence

$$x \cdot s(y) = x \cdot y + x = x * y + x = x * s(y),$$

and so $s(y) \in M_x$. Therefore $y \in M_x$ implies $s(y) \in M_x$.

We observe that

$$x \cdot 1 = x = x * 1,$$

from which it follows that $1 \in M_x$.

Therefore $M_x = \textbf{N}$ for every $x \in \textbf{N}$. That is,

$$x \cdot y = x * y$$

for every $x \in \textbf{N}$ and every $y \in \textbf{N}$. Hence there is at most one such binary operation.

Next we shall show that there exists *at least* one such operation on **N**. Let M be the set of all natural numbers x for which there exists a mapping g_x of **N** into itself such that

$$g_x(1) = x,$$

and

$$g_x(s(y)) = g_x(y) + x \qquad \text{for every} \quad y \in \textbf{N}.$$

Assume that $x \in M$. Then a mapping g_x having the above properties exists. Let

$$\phi(u) = g_x(u) + u \qquad \text{for every} \quad u \in \textbf{N}.$$

Then

$$\phi(1) = g_x(1) + 1 = x + 1 = s(x),$$

and

$$\phi(s(y)) = g_x(s(y)) + s(y) = (g_x(y) + x) + s(y)$$

$$\phi(s(y)) = g_x(y) + (x + s(y)) = g_x(y) + s(x + y)$$
$$= g_x(y) + (s(x) + y) = g_x(y) + (y + s(x))$$
$$= (g_x(y) + y) + s(x)$$
$$= \phi(y) + s(x) \qquad \text{for every} \quad y \in \mathbf{N}.$$

Therefore ϕ has the properties required of $g_{s(x)}$, and so $g_{s(x)}$ exists. Therefore $s(x) \in M$. Hence $x \in M$ implies $s(x) \in M$.

Let $\psi(u) = u$ for every $u \in N$. Then $\psi(1) = 1$, and

$$\psi(s(y)) = s(y) = y + 1 = \psi(y) + 1 \qquad \text{for every} \quad y \in \mathbf{N}.$$

Therefore ψ has the properties required of g_1, and so g_1 exists. Therefore $1 \in M$.

It follows from the principle of finite induction that $M = \mathbf{N}$. That is, such a mapping g_x exists for every $x \in \mathbf{N}$.

Let

$$x \cdot y = g_x(y). \qquad \text{for every} \quad x \in \mathbf{N}, y \in \mathbf{N}.$$

Then

$$x \cdot 1 = g_x(1) = x \qquad \text{for every} \quad x \in \mathbf{N},$$

and

$$x \cdot s(y) = g_x(s(y)) = g_x(y) + x = x \cdot y + x \qquad \text{for every} \quad x \in \mathbf{N}, y \in \mathbf{N}.$$

Therefore there is at least one such binary operation on $\mathbf{N}$, and hence exactly one. $\square$

13   DEFINITION

The unique binary operation $\cdot$ on $\mathbf{N}$ whose existence is guaranteed by Theorem 12 will be called *multiplication*. For each $x \in \mathbf{N}$ and each $y \in \mathbf{N}$ the natural number $x \cdot y$ will be called the *product* of x and y. (Henceforth we shall usually omit the sign $\cdot$ in expressions such as "$x \cdot y$", and use instead xy.)

14   COROLLARY

Multiplication of natural numbers has the following properties:

[1] $1 \cdot y = y$ for every $y \in \mathbf{N}$, and
[2] $s(x) \cdot y = xy + y$ for every $x \in \mathbf{N}$ and every $y \in \mathbf{N}$.

Proof

In the second (existence) part of the proof of Theorem 12 it was shown that $xy = g_x(y)$, where $g_1(u) = u$ for every $u \in \mathbf{N}$ and $g_{s(x)}(u) = g_x(u) + u$ for every $u \in \mathbf{N}$. Therefore

$$1 \cdot y = g_1(y) = y \qquad \text{for every} \quad y \in \mathbf{N},$$

and

$$s(x) \cdot y = g_{s(x)}(y) = g_x(y) + y = xy + y \qquad \text{for every} \quad x \in \mathbf{N}, y \in \mathbf{N}. \quad \square$$

15 THEOREM Commutative Law of Multiplication

For every $x \in \mathbf{N}$ and every $y \in \mathbf{N}$,

$$xy = yx.$$

Proof

For fixed but arbitrary $y \subset \mathbf{N}$ let

$$M_y = \{x \in \mathbf{N} : xy = yx\}.$$

Assume that $x \in M_y$. Then $xy = yx$. Hence

$$s(x) \cdot y = xy + y \qquad \text{C14}$$

$$= yx + y$$

$$= y \cdot s(x) \qquad \text{T12}$$

and so $s(x) \in M_y$. Therefore $x \in M_y$ implies $s(x) \in M_y$.

It follows at once from Corollary 14 and Theorem 12 that

$$1 \cdot y = y = y \cdot 1,$$

and so $1 \in M_y$.

Therefore $M_y = \mathbf{N}$ for every $y \in \mathbf{N}$. $\quad \square$

16 THEOREM Distributive Law of Multiplication over Addition

For every $x \in \mathbf{N}$, every $y \in \mathbf{N}$, and every $z \in \mathbf{N}$,

$$x(y + z) = xy + xz.$$

Proof

For fixed but arbitrary x and y in $\mathbf{N}$, let

$$M_{xy} = \{z \in \mathbf{N} : x(y + z) = xy + xz\}.$$

Assume that $z \in M_{xy}$. Then $x(y + z) = xy + xz$. Hence

$$x(y + s(z)) = x(s(y + z)) \qquad \text{T6}$$

$$= x(y + z) + x \qquad \text{T12}$$

$$= (xy + xz) + x$$

$$= xy + (xz + x) \qquad \text{T10}$$

$$= xy + x \cdot s(z) \qquad \text{T12}$$

and so $s(z) \in M_{xy}$. Therefore $z \in M_{xy}$ implies $s(z) \in M_{xy}$.
   Also

$$x(y + 1) = x \cdot s(y) \qquad \text{T6}$$

$$= xy + x \qquad \text{T12}$$

$$= xy + x \cdot 1 \qquad \text{T12}$$

and so $1 \in M_{xy}$.
   Therefore $M_{xy} = \mathbf{N}$ for every $x \in \mathbf{N}$ and every $y \in \mathbf{N}$. $\square$

17   THEOREM   Associative Law of Multiplication

For every $x \in \mathbf{N}$, every $y \in \mathbf{N}$, and every $z \in \mathbf{N}$, $(xy)z = x(yz)$.
Proof
For fixed but arbitrary x and y in $\mathbf{N}$ let

$$M_{xy} = \{z \in \mathbf{N} : (xy)z = x(yz)\}.$$

Assume that $z \in M_{xy}$. Then $(xy)z = x(yz)$. Hence

$$(xy) \cdot s(z) = (xy)z + xy \qquad \text{T12}$$

$$= x(yz) + xy$$

$$= x(yz + y) \qquad \text{T16}$$

$$= x(y \cdot s(z)) \qquad \text{T12}$$

and so $s(z) \in M_{xy}$. Therefore $z \in M_{xy}$ implies $s(z) \in M_{xy}$.
   Furthermore

$$(xy) \cdot 1 = xy \qquad \text{T12}$$

$$= x(y \cdot 1) \qquad \text{T12}$$

so $1 \in M_{xy}$.

   Therefore $M_{xy} = \mathbf{N}$ for every $x \in \mathbf{N}$ and every $y \in \mathbf{N}$. $\square$

EXERCISES

1   ▷ Prove that for all x, y, and z in **N**,

$$(x + y)z = xz + yz.$$

2   Let 2, 3, 4, 5, and 6 denote the natural numbers $s(1)$, $s(2)$, $s(3)$, $s(4)$, and $s(5)$, respectively. Prove that $2 \cdot 2 = 4$ and that $3 \cdot 2 = 6$.

3   (a) Formulate a definition for "even natural number."
        (b) Formulate a definition for "odd natural number."
        (c) Let x and y be natural numbers. Formulate a definition for "x is a factor of y." Use the notation $x|y$ to denote that x is a factor of y.
        (d) Prove that if $x \in$ **N**, then $1|x$ and $x|x$.

Order in the Set **N**

The definition that we shall give for "greater than" asserts (in view of the commutative law of addition) that the sum of two natural numbers is greater than either of them. Regarded in this light, the definition seems quite natural. The comparability of every pair of natural numbers, however, is not exactly a trivial consequence of the definition.

18   **DEFINITION**

Let x and y be natural numbers. We shall say that x is *greater than y*, denoted by $x > y$, iff there is a $u \in$ **N** such that $x = y + u$. We shall say that x is *less than y*, denoted by $x < y$, iff there is a $v \in$ **N** such that $x + v = y$.

19   **THEOREM**

If x and y are in **N**, then $x > y$ if and only if $y < x$.

Proof

If $x < y$, then there is a $u \in$ **N** such that $x = y + u$. But then $y + u = x$, and so $y < x$. Conversely, if $y < x$, then there is a $v \in$ **N** such that $y + v = x$. But then $x = y + v$, and so $x > y$. $\square$

20   THEOREM   Trichotomy Law

For given natural numbers x and y exactly one of the following is true:

$$y < x, \quad y = x, \quad \text{or} \quad y > x.$$

Proof

For fixed but arbitrary $x \in \mathbf{N}$, let

$$L_x = \{y \in \mathbf{N} : y < x\},$$

and let

$$G_x = \{y \in \mathbf{N} : y > x\}.$$

S_5 Finally, let $M_x = (L_x \cup G_x) \cup \{x\}$. We shall show that $M_x = \mathbf{N}$.

Assume $y \in M_x$. Then either $y \in L_x$, $y \in G_x$, or $y \in \{x\}$; that is, either $y < x$, $y > x$, or $y = x$.

[1] If $y < x$, then there is a $v \in \mathbf{N}$ such that $y + v = x$. Now either $v = 1$ or $v = s(w)$ for some $w \in N$. If $v = 1$ then $x = y + 1 = s(y)$, so $s(y) \in \{x\}$, whence $s(y) \in M_x$. If $v = s(w)$, then

$$x = y + s(w) = y + (1 + w) = (y + 1) + w = s(y) + w,$$

which implies that $s(y) < x$, so $s(y) \in L_x$, whence $s(y) \in M_x$.

[2] If $y > x$, then there is a $u \in N$ such that $y = x + u$. Then

$$s(y) = s(x + u) = x + s(u),$$

and so $s(y) > x$. Hence $s(y) \in G_x$, whence $s(y) \in M_x$.

[3] If $y = x$, then

$$s(y) = s(x) = x + 1,$$

and so $s(y) > x$. Hence $s(y) \in G_x$, whence $s(y) \in M_x$.

Therefore $y \in M_x$ implies $s(y) \in M_x$.

If $x = 1$, then $1 \in \{x\}$, whence $1 \in M_x$. If $x \neq 1$, then there is a $z \in N$ such that $x \in s(z) = 1 + z$, and so $1 < x$. Therefore $1 \in L_x$, whence $1 \in M_x$. Therefore $1 \in M_x$. Therefore $M_x = \mathbf{N}$ for every $x \in \mathbf{N}$.

Hence, for every $x \in \mathbf{N}$ and every $y \in \mathbf{N}$, *at least* one of the statements $y < x$, $y = x$, $y > x$ is true. The proof that at most one of them is true for given x and y is an easy consequence of Exercise 3, p. 8 and is left as an exercise for the reader. $\square$

21   THEOREM   Transitive Law

If x, y, and z are natural numbers such that $x > y$ and $y > z$, then $x > z$.

Proof

Since $x > y$ and $y > z$, there are natural numbers u and v such that $x = y + u$ and $y = z + v$.

Hence

$$x = y + u = (z + v) + u = z + (v + u),$$

and so $x > z$.

22   DEFINITION

The notation $x \geq y$ means that either $x > y$ or $x = y$. Similarly, $x \leq y$ means that either $x < y$ or $x = y$.

23   THEOREM

For every $x \in$ **N**, $x \geq 1$.

Proof

If $x \neq 1$, then $x = s(u)$ for some $u \in$ **N**. Hence

$$x = s(u) = 1 + u,$$

from which it follows that $x > 1$. ☐

24   THEOREM

If x and y are natural numbers such that $x < y$, then $x + 1 \leq y$.

Proof

Since $x < y$, there is a $v \in$ **N** such that $x + v = y$. If $v = 1$, then $x + 1 = y$. If $v \neq 1$, then $v = s(w)$ for some $w \in$ **N**, and so

$$y = x + v = x + s(w) = x + (1 + w) = (x + 1) + w,$$

whence $x + 1 < y$. ☐

25   THEOREM

Every nonempty set of natural numbers contains a smallest element.

That is, if S is a nonempty subset of $\mathbf{N}$, then there exists $x_0 \in S$ such that

$$x_0 \leq y \qquad \text{for every} \quad y \in S.$$

Proof

Let S be a nonempty set of natural numbers, and let

$$M = \{x \in \mathbf{N} : x \leq y \qquad \text{for every} \quad y \in S\}.$$

Now $1 \in M$ because $1 \leq y$ for every $y \in N$, and so $1 \leq y$ for every $y \in S$.

The set S is not empty, so there is a natural number $z_0 \in S$. Since $s(z_0) = z_0 + 1 > z_0$, it follows that $s(z_0) \notin M$. Therefore $M \neq \mathbf{N}$.

Since $1 \in M$ but $M \neq \mathbf{N}$, it follows from the principle of finite induction that there is a number x_0 such that $x_0 \in M$ but $s(x_0) \notin M$.

Now $x_0 \leq y$ for every $y \in S$ because $x_0 \in M$. The proof will be completed by showing that $x_0 \in S$.

Assume that $x_0 \notin S$. Then $x_0 < y$ for every $y \in S$. Hence, by Theorem 24, $x_0 + 1 \leq y$ for every $y \in S$, and so $s(x_0) \leq y$ for every $y \in S$. Therefore $s(x_0) \in M$. But this contradicts the fact that $s(x_0) \notin M$. Hence $x_0 \in S$. □

EXERCISES

1   Complete the proof of Theorem 20.

2   Prove that if $x \in \mathbf{N}$, then $yx \geq x$ for every $y \in \mathbf{N}$.

3   If x, y, and z are natural numbers, prove that $x + z > y + z$ if and only if $x > y$.

4   ▷ Prove that for no $x \in \mathbf{N}$ is it true that there exists a $y \in \mathbf{N}$ such that $x < y < s(x)$.

5   This is a continuation of Exercise 3, p. 13.
   (a) Formulate a definition for "prime natural number."
   (b) Prove that the only even natural number that is prime is $s(1)$.

6   Prove that if x and y are natural numbers with $x > y$, then there exists a *unique* $u \in \mathbf{N}$ such that $x = y + u$.

7   Prove that if y and z are natural numbers with $y > z$, then $xy > xz$ for every $x \in \mathbf{N}$.

8   Prove the *Multiplicative Cancellation Law*: If x, y, and z are natural numbers such that $xy = xz$, then $y = z$.

9   Prove that if $x \in$ **N** and $y \in$ **N**, then there is a $z \in$ **N** such that $zx > y$.

10   Prove that if $x \in$ **N**, $y \in$ **N**, and $x < y$, then either
(a) there is a $q \in$ **N** such that $qx = y$, or
(b) there are natural numbers q and r with $r < x$ such that $qx + r = y$.

11 ▷ Prove the so-called *Second Principle of Induction*: If M is a subset of **N** that has both of the following properties:
(a) $x \in$ **N** and $y \in M$ for every $y \in$ **N** with $y < x$ imply that $x \in M$, and
(b) $1 \in M$,
then $M =$ **N**.

The Integers

A₁   It is quite easy to see that the set **N** of natural numbers is not a group relative to addition: If x is any natural number it follows from Definition 18 that $x + y > x$ for every $y \in$ **N**. Hence the set **N** contains no identity element relative to addition.

We shall now construct from **N** a new system of numbers that *is* a group relative to addition. We shall also define multiplication and order in our new system of numbers, and we shall see that this new

A₇   system is, in fact, an *ordered integral domain* containing a copy of **N**.

The method of construction is based on the following informal observations. Say, for example, that we wish to associate with the

S₉   *ordered pair* of natural numbers (2, 5) an entirely new kind of number, one which we might choose to designate as ⁻3. Now it is intuitively clear that ⁻3 ought to be associated not only with the ordered pair (2, 5), but also with ordered pairs such as (5, 8), (1, 4), and (7, 10). What property, *expressible in terms of the arithmetic of* **N**, do these ordered pairs have in common? Consider (2, 5) and (5, 8); note that $2 + 8 = 5 + 5$. Consider (1, 4) and (7, 10); note that $1 + 10 = 4 + 7$. Consider (1, 4) and (2, 5); note that $1 + 5 = 4 + 2$.

26   DEFINITION

Let (a, b) and (c, d) be ordered pairs of natural numbers. We shall say that (a, b) is *equivalent* to (c, d), denoted by $(a, b) \approx (c, d)$, iff $a + d = b + c$.

27   THEOREM

S$_{11}$ The *relation* $\lessgtr$ is an *equivalence relation* on **N** $\times$ **N**.

S$_{12}$ Proof

S$_{10}$ It follows from the commutative law of addition that $a + b = b + a$.
Hence $(a, b) \lessgtr (a, b)$ for all $(a, b) \in$ **N** $\times$ **N**. Therefore $\lessgtr$ is reflexive.

If $(a, b) \lessgtr (c, d)$, then $a + d = b + c$. Hence, by the commutative
law of addition, $d + a = c + b$. Therefore $c + b = d + a$, and so
$(c, d) \lessgtr (a, b)$. Hence $\lessgtr$ is symmetric.

If $(a, b) \lessgtr (c, d)$ and $(c, d) \lessgtr (e, f)$, then

$$a + d = b + c \quad \text{and} \quad c + f = d + e.$$

Therefore

$$(a + d) + (c + f) = (b + c) + (d + e).$$

Following several applications of the commutative and associative laws
of addition, this equation becomes

$$(c + d) + (a + f) = (c + d) + (b + e).$$

Applying the additive cancellation law, we obtain

$$a + f = b + e.$$

Therefore $(a, b) \lessgtr (e, f)$. Hence $\lessgtr$ is transitive. $\square$

28   LEMMA

[1] If $n \in$ **N**, $m \in$ **N**, and $m \neq n$, then $(n, 1)$ is not equivalent to $(m, 1)$,
and $(1, n)$ is not equivalent to $(1, m)$. [2] For every $n \in$ **N** and every
$m \in$ **N**, $(s(n), 1)$ is not equivalent to $(1, s(m))$.

Proof

[1] Assume that $(n, 1) \lessgtr (m, 1)$ for some $n \in$ **N** and some $m \in$ **N**.
Then $n + 1 = 1 + m$, so $1 + n = 1 + m$, whence $n = m$. Similarly, if
$(1, n) \lessgtr (1, m)$ for some $n \in$ **N** and some $m \in$ **N**, then $1 + m = n + 1$, so
$1 + n = 1 + m$, whence $m = n$. Hence if $n \neq m$, then $(n, 1)$ is not
equivalent to $(m, 1)$, and $(1, n)$ is not equivalent to $(1, m)$.

[2] Assume that $(s(n), 1) \lessgtr (1, s(m))$ for some $n \in$ **N** and some
$m \in$ **N**. Then

$$s(n) + s(m) = 1 + 1,$$

and so

$$(n + 1) + (m + 1) = 1 + 1.$$

Applying the associative and commutative laws of addition several times to the left member of this equation, we obtain

$$1 + ((n + m) + 1) = 1 + 1,$$

from which it follows that

$$(n + m) + 1 = 1.$$

Therefore, by Definition 18, $n + m < 1$. This is a contradiction of Theorem 23. Therefore, for every $n \in M$ and every $m \in \mathbf{N}$, $(s(n), 1)$ is not equivalent to $(1, s(m))$. $\square$

29 DEFINITION

S₁₃ For each natural number n we define the *positive integer* ^+n (read "positive n") to be the $\lessgtr$-*equivalence class* containing the ordered pair $(s(n), 1)$, and we define the *negative integer* ^-n (read "negative n") to be the $\lessgtr$-equivalence class containing the ordered pair $(1, s(n))$. We define the integer 0 (read "zero") to be the $\lessgtr$-equivalence class containing the ordered pair $(1, 1)$. Finally, we define the set $\mathbf{Z}$ of all integers to be

$$\{^+n : n \in \mathbf{N}\} \cup \{^-n : n \in \mathbf{N}\} \cup \{0\}.$$

In the work that follows, we shall shorten the notation for the $\lessgtr$-equivalence class containing the ordered pair (a, b) from the strictly correct $[(a, b)]$ to the more convenient $[a, b]$.

30 THEOREM

If n and m are natural numbers with $n \neq m$, then $^+n \neq {}^+m$ and $^-n \neq {}^-m$.

Proof

Since $n \neq m$, it follows from Theorem 1 that $s(n) \neq s(m)$. Hence, by Lemma 28, $(s(n), 1)$ is not equivalent to $(s(m), 1)$, and $(1, s(n))$ is not equivalent to $(1, s(m))$. Therefore $[s(n), 1] \neq [s(m), 1]$, and $[1, s(n)] \neq [1, s(m)]$. Hence $^+n \neq {}^+m$, and $^-n \neq {}^-m$. $\square$

31 THEOREM

For given $x \in \mathbf{Z}$, exactly one of the following statements is true: $x = {}^+n$ for a unique $n \in \mathbf{N}$, $x = 0$, or $x = {}^-m$ for a unique $m \in \mathbf{N}$.

Proof

That at least one of the statements is true for a given $x \in \mathbf{Z}$ follows from Definition 29 and Theorem 30.

[1] Assume that $x = {}^+n$ for some $n \in \mathbf{N}$ and also that $x = 0$. Then $[s(n), 1] = [1, 1]$, and so $(s(n), 1) \gtrless (1, 1)$. Since $s(n) \neq 1$, this contradicts Lemma 28.

[2] Assume that $x = {}^+n$ for some $n \in \mathbf{N}$ and also that $x = {}^-m$ for some $m \in \mathbf{N}$. Then $[s(n), 1] = [1, s(m)]$, and so $(s(n), 1) \gtrless (1, s(m))$. This contradicts Lemma 28.

[3] Assume that $x = 0$ and also that $x = {}^-m$ for some $m \in \mathbf{N}$. Then $[1, 1] = [1, s(m)]$, and so $(1, 1) \gtrless (1, s(m))$. Since $s(m) \neq 1$, this contradicts Lemma 28.

Hence for given $x \in \mathbf{Z}$, at most one of the statements is true. ☐

32   THEOREM

For every $a \in \mathbf{N}$ and every $b \in \mathbf{N}$, $[a, b] \in \mathbf{Z}$.

Proof

If $a \in \mathbf{N}$ and $b \in \mathbf{N}$, then it follows from the trichotomy law for $\mathbf{N}$ that either $a < b$, $a = b$, or $a > b$.

[1] Assume that $a < b$. Then $a + m = b$ for some $m \in \mathbf{N}$. Hence

$$a + s(m) = a + (m + 1) = (a + m) + 1 = b + 1,$$

and so $(a, b) \gtrless (1, s(m))$. Therefore

$$[a, b] = [1, s(m)] = {}^-m,$$

and so $[a, b] \in \mathbf{Z}$.

[2] Assume that $a = b$. Then $a + 1 = b + 1$, and so $(a, b) \gtrless (1, 1)$. Hence $[a, b] = 0$, and so $[a, b] \in \mathbf{Z}$.

[3] Assume that $a > b$. Then $a = b + n$ for some $n \in \mathbf{N}$. Hence

$$a + 1 = (b + n) + 1 = b + (n + 1) = b + s(n),$$

whence $(a, b) \gtrless (s(n), 1)$. Therefore

$$[a, b] = [s(n), 1] = {}^+n,$$

and so $[a, b] \in \mathbf{Z}$. ☐

33   COROLLARY

Let a and b be natural numbers. Then

$[a, b] = {}^+n$ for some $n \in \mathbf{N}$ if and only if $a > b$,

$[a, b] = 0$ if and only if $a = b$,

and

$[a, b] = {}^-m$ for some $m \in \mathbf{N}$ if and only if $a < b$.

Proof

The "if" part of each assertion was established in the proof of Theorem 32. The "only if" parts follow from the trichotomy law for **N** and Theorem 31. That is, for example, if $[a, b] = {}^+n$ for some $n \in \mathbf{N}$, then $a \neq b$ because $a = b$ implies that $[a, b] = 0$ (a contradiction of Theorem 31); and a is not less than b, because $a < b$ implies $[a, b] = {}^-m$ for some $m \in \mathbf{N}$ (another contradiction of Theorem 31). Hence, by the trichotomy law, $a > b$. $\square$

34   DEFINITION

Given integers x and y, let a, b, c, and d be natural numbers such that $x = [a, b]$ and $y = [c, d]$. We define the *sum* of x and y, denoted by $x + y$, by

$$x + y = [a + c, b + d].$$

We define the *product* of x and y, denoted by $x \cdot y$ or xy, by

$$x \cdot y = [ac + bd, ad + bc].$$

35   LEMMA

S_{19} The operations $+$ and $\cdot$ are *well defined* on the set **Z**. That is, if $(a, b) \gtrless (p, q)$ and $(c, d) \gtrless (r, s)$, then

$$(a + c, b + d) \gtrless (p + r, q + s),$$

and

$$(ac + bd, ad + bc) \gtrless (pr + qs, ps + qr).$$

Proof

Assume that $(a, b) \gtrless (p, q)$ and $(c, d) \gtrless (r, s)$. Then $a + q = b + p$ and $c + s = d + r$. Hence

$$(a + q) + (c + s) = (b + p) + (d + r).$$

From this it follows that

$$(a + c) + (q + s) = (b + d) + (p + r).$$

Therefore $(a + c, b + d) \gtreqless (p + r, q + s)$.

[2] Assume again that $(a, b) \gtreqless (p, q)$ and $(c, d) \gtreqless (r, s)$. This implies, as before, that $a + q = b + p$ and $c + s = d + r$.

(a) Suppose $a < b$. Then $b = a + v$ for some $v \in \mathbf{N}$. Hence

$$a + q = b + p = (a + v) + p = a + (v + p).$$

Therefore

$$q = v + p = p + v.$$

We then have

$$
\begin{aligned}
(ac + bd) + (ps + qr) &= (ac + (a + v)d) + (ps + (p + v)r) \\
&= (ac + (ad + vd)) + (ps + (pr + vr)) \\
&= (a(c + d) + p(s + r)) + v(d + r),
\end{aligned}
$$

and

$$
\begin{aligned}
(ad + bc) + (pr + qs) &= (ad + (a + v)c) + (pr + (p + v)s) \\
&= (ad + (ac + vc)) + (pr + (ps + vs)) \\
&= (a(c + d) + p(s + r)) + v(c + s) \\
&= (a(c + d) + p(s + r)) + v(d + r),
\end{aligned}
$$

since, by hypothesis, $c + s = d + r$. Therefore

$$(ac + bd) + (ps + qr) = (ad + bc) + (pr + qs),$$

and so

$$(ac + bd, ad + bc) \gtreqless (pr + qs, ps + qr).$$

(b) Assume $a = b$. Then

$$b + p = a + q = b + q,$$

and so $p = q$. We then have

$$
\begin{aligned}
(ac + bd) + (ps + qr) &= (ac + ad) + (ps + pr) \\
&= a(c + d) + p(s + r),
\end{aligned}
$$

and

$$
\begin{aligned}
(ad + bc) + (pr + qs) &= (ad + ac) + (ps + pr) \\
&= a(d + c) + p(s + r).
\end{aligned}
$$

Therefore

$$(ac + bd) + (ps + qr) = (ad + bc) + (pr + qs),$$

whence

$$(ac + bd, ad + bc) \gtrless (pr + qs, ps + qr).$$

(c) Finally, suppose that $a > b$. Then $a = b + u$ for some $u \in \mathbf{N}$. Hence

$$b + p = a + q = (b + u) + q = b + (u + q).$$

Therefore

$$p = u + q = q + u.$$

We then have

$$(ac + bd) + (ps + qr) = ((b + u)c + bd) + ((q + u)s + qr)$$
$$= (b(c + d) + q(s + r)) + u(c + s),$$

and

$$(ad + bc) + (pr + qs) = ((b + u)d + bc) + ((q + u)r + qs)$$
$$= (b(c + d) + q(s + r)) + u(d + r)$$
$$= (b(c + d) + q(s + r)) + u(c + s),$$

since $c + s = d + r$ by hypothesis. Hence

$$(ac + bd) + (ps + qr) = (ad + bc) + (pr + qs),$$

and so

$$(ac + bd, ad + bc) \gtrless (pr + qs, ps + qr). \quad \square$$

EXERCISES

1   Use Definition 34 to calculate each of the following:

(a) $^+3 + {}^-2$ (b) $^-4 + {}^-2$ (c) $^+3 \cdot {}^-2$
(d) $^-2 \cdot {}^-2$ (e) $^+3 \cdot {}^+1$ (f) $^-1 \cdot {}^+2$.

2   Prove that for every a, b, c, and d in $\mathbf{N}$,

$$(a, b) \gtrless (c, d) \quad \text{if and only if} \quad (a, c) \gtrless (b, d),$$
$$(a, b) \gtrless (c, d) \quad \text{if and only if} \quad (b, a) \gtrless (d, c),$$

and

$$(a, b) \gtrless (c, d) \quad \text{if and only if} \quad (d, b) \gtrless (c, a).$$

3   ▷ Prove that for every a, b, and c in $\mathbf{N}$,

$$(a + c, b + c) \gtrless (a, b).$$

4   Formulate a definition for "the difference of the integers x and y." Show that your definition is a "good" one by stating and proving a lemma similar to Lemma 35. [Such a definition be- comes available "free of charge" when we have proved that $(\mathbf{Z}; +, \cdot)$ is an *integral domain*. In the meantime, a suitable definition *can* be given directly in terms of ordered pairs of natural numbers.]

A_4

Properties of Sums and Products of Integers

36   THEOREM   Commutative Laws

For every $x \in \mathbf{Z}$ and every $y \in \mathbf{Z}$,

$$x + y = y + x,$$

and

$$xy = yx.$$

Proof

For given x and y in $\mathbf{Z}$ let a, b, c, and d be natural numbers such that $x = [a, b]$ and $y = [c, d]$. Then

$$x + y = [a, b] + [c, d] = [a + c, b + d]$$

$$= [c + a, d + b] = [c, d] + [a, b] = y + x,$$

and

$$xy = [a, b][c, d] = [ac + bd, ad + bc]$$

$$= [ca + db, da + cb]$$

$$= [ca + db, cb + da]$$

$$= [c, d][a, b] = yx. \quad \square$$

37   THEOREM   Associative Laws

For every x, y, and z in $\mathbf{Z}$,

$$(x + y) + z = x + (y + z),$$

and

$$(xy)z = x(yz).$$

Proof

For given x, y, and z in $\mathbf{Z}$ let a, b, c, d, e, and f be natural numbers such that $x = [a, b]$, $y = [c, d]$, and $z = [e, f]$. Then

$$(x + y) + z = ([a, b] + [c, d]) + ([e, f])$$
$$= [a + c, b + d] + [e, f]$$
$$= [(a + c) + e, (b + d) + f]$$
$$= [a + (c + e), b + (d + f)]$$
$$= [a, b] + [c + e, d + f]$$
$$= x + ([c, d] + [e, f]) = x + (y + z),$$

and

$$(xy)z = ([a, b][c, d])([e, f])$$
$$= [ac + bd, ad + bc][e, f]$$
$$= [(ac + bd)e + (ad + bc)f, (ac + bd)f + (ad + bc)e]$$
$$= [a(ce + df) + b(de + cf), a(cf + de) + b(df + ce)]$$
$$= [a(ce + df) + b(cf + de), a(cf + de) + b(ce + df)]$$
$$= [a, b][ce + df, cf + de]$$
$$= x([c, d][e, f]) = x(yz). \quad \square$$

38   THEOREM   Distributive Law of Multiplication over Addition

For every x, y, and z in $\mathbf{Z}$,

$$x(y + z) = xy + xz.$$

Proof

For given x, y, and z in $\mathbf{Z}$ let a, b, c, d, e, and f be natural numbers such that $x = [a, b]$, $y = [c, d]$, and $z = [e, f]$. Then

$$x(y + z) = [a, b]([c, d] + [e, f])$$
$$= [a, b][c + e, d + f]$$
$$= [a(c + e) + b(d + f), a(d + f) + b(c + e)]$$
$$= [(ac + ae) + (bd + bf), (ad + af) + (bc + be)]$$
$$= [(ac + bd) + (ae + bf), (ad + bc) + (af + be)]$$
$$= [ac + bd, ad + bc] + [ae + bf, af + be]$$

$$x(y + z) = [a, b][c, d] + [a, b][e, f]$$

$$= xy + xz. \quad \square$$

39   THEOREM

For every $x \in \mathbf{Z}$, $x \cdot {}^{+}1 = x$.

Proof

For a given $x \in \mathbf{Z}$, let a and b be natural numbers such that $x = [a, b]$. Then

$$x \cdot {}^{+}1 = [a, b][s(1), 1]$$

$$= [a \cdot s(1) + b, a + b \cdot s(1)]$$

$$= [(a \cdot 1 + a) + b, a + (b \cdot 1 + b)]$$

$$= [(a + a) + b, a + (b + b)]$$

$$= [a + (a + b), b + (a + b)].$$

Now it follows from Exercise 3, p.23 that

$$(a + (a + b), b + (a + b)) \gtreqless (a, b).$$

Hence

$$x \cdot {}^{+}1 = [a + (a + b), b + (a + b)] = [a, b] = x. \quad \square$$

40   THEOREM

For every $x \in \mathbf{Z}$, $x + 0 = x$.

Proof

For given $x \in \mathbf{Z}$, let a and b be natural numbers such that $x = [a, b]$. Then

$$x + 0 = [a, b] + [1, 1]$$

$$= [a + 1, b + 1].$$

But $(a + 1, b + 1) \gtreqless (a, b)$, because $(a + 1) + b = (b + 1) + a$. Hence $x + 0 = [a + 1, b + 1] = [a, b] = x. \quad \square$

41   THEOREM

For every $m \in \mathbf{N}$ and every $n \in \mathbf{N}$,

$$^{+}m \cdot {}^{+}n = {}^{+}mn,$$

$$^{+}m \cdot {}^{-}n = {}^{-}m \cdot {}^{+}n = {}^{-}(mn),$$

and

$$(^-m)(^-n) = {}^+(mn).$$

Proof

$$
\begin{aligned}
{}^+m \cdot {}^+n &= [s(m), 1][s(n), 1] \\
&= [s(m) \cdot s(n) + 1, s(m) + s(n)] \\
&= [(s(m) \cdot n) + s(m) + 1, s(s(m) + n)] \\
&= [(mn + n) + s(m) + 1, s(s(m) + n)] \\
&= [(mn + 1) + (s(m) + n), 1 + (s(m) + n)] \\
&= [s(mn) + s(m + n), 1 + s(m + n)]
\end{aligned}
$$

But $(s(mn) + s(m + n), 1 + s(m + n)) \gtrless (s(mn), 1)$. Therefore ${}^+m \cdot {}^+n = [s(mn), 1] = {}^+(mn)$.

The proofs of the remaining assertions of the theorem are left as exercises for the reader. ☐

42 THEOREM

For every $m \in \mathbf{N}$ and every $n \in \mathbf{N}$,

$$ {}^+m + {}^+n = {}^+(m + n).$$

Proof

$$
\begin{aligned}
{}^+m + {}^+n &= [s(m), 1] + [s(n), 1] \\
&= [s(m) + s(n), 1 + 1] \\
&= [s(s(m) + n), 1 + 1] \\
&= [(s(m) + n) + 1, 1 + 1] \\
&= [s(m + n) + 1, 1 + 1].
\end{aligned}
$$

But $(s(m + n) + 1, 1 + 1) \gtrless (s(m + n), 1)$, and so ${}^+m + {}^+n = [s(m + n), 1] = {}^+(m + n)$. ☐

43 THEOREM

Let x and y be integers. Then $xy = 0$ if and only if either $x = 0$ or $y = 0$.

Proof

[1] For given $x \in \mathbf{Z}$ let a and b be natural numbers such that $x = [a, b]$. Then $x \cdot 0 = [a, b][1, 1] = [a + b, a + b]$. It follows from Corollary 33 that $x \cdot 0 = 0$ for every $x \in \mathbf{Z}$. Also $0 \cdot y = y \cdot 0 = 0$ by the

commutative law of multiplication and the first paragraph of this proof. Hence if $x = 0$ or $y = 0$, then $xy = 0$.

[2] Now assume that $x \neq 0$ and $y \neq 0$. Then, by Theorem 31, either $x = {}^+m$ or $x = {}^-m$ for some $m \in$ **N**, and either $y = {}^+n$ or $y = {}^-n$ for some $n \in$ **N**. It follows from Theorem 41 that xy is either ${}^+(mn)$ or ${}^-(mn)$, whence $xy \neq 0$. Hence if $xy = 0$, then either $x = 0$ or $y = 0$. $\square$

EXERCISES

1   Complete the proof of Theorem 41.

2   Prove that for every $m \in$ **N** and every $n \in$ **N**, ${}^-m + {}^-n = {}^-(m + n)$.

3   ▷ Prove that for every $n \in$ **N**, ${}^+n + {}^-n = 0$.

The Integers as an Ordered Integral Domain

The astute reader has probably observed that the properties we have established for sums and products form a rather large subset of the set of all properties required of an ordered integral domain. In fact, only one more definition is required to achieve the objectives outlined at the beginning of our discussion of the integers.

44   DEFINITION

Let x be an integer. Then the *opposite* (or *additive inverse*) of x, denoted by $-x$, is defined as follows:

$$-x = \begin{cases} {}^-n & \text{if } x = {}^+n \text{ for some } n \in \textbf{N} \\ 0 & \text{if } x = 0 \\ {}^+m & \text{if } x = {}^-m \text{ for some } m \in \textbf{N}. \end{cases}$$

Our next theorem is an immediate consequence of Definition 44, Theorem 40, and Exercise 3, above.

45   THEOREM

For every $x \in$ **Z**, $x + (-x) = 0$.

46 THEOREM

S_{16} Let $P = \{^{+}n : n \in \mathbf{N}\}$. Then $(\mathbf{Z}; +, \cdot \, ; P)$ is an *ordered integral domain.*
A_{17} Furthermore there exists a *one-to-one, order-preserving mapping* of $\mathbf{N}$
A_{13} onto P that also preserves sums and products (that is, the system of
A_{14} integers contains a *copy* of the system of natural numbers).

Proof

Theorems 36, 37, 38, 40, 43, and 45 imply that $(Z; +, \cdot)$ is an integral
domain. Theorems 31, 41, 42, and Definition 44 then imply $(Z; +, \cdot \, ; P)$
is an ordered integral domain.

For each $n \in \mathbf{N}$, let $\alpha(n) = {}^{+}n$. Then α is a one-to-one mapping of
$\mathbf{N}$ onto P (Theorem 30). Furthermore

$$\alpha(m + n) = {}^{+}(m + n) = {}^{+}m + {}^{+}n \qquad \text{T42}$$

$$= \alpha(m) + \alpha(n), \qquad \text{for every} \quad m \text{ and } n \text{ in } \mathbf{N},$$

and

$$\alpha(mn) = {}^{+}(mn) = {}^{+}m \cdot {}^{+}n \qquad \text{T41}$$

$$= \alpha(m) \cdot \alpha(n) \qquad \text{for every} \quad m \text{ and } n \text{ in } \mathbf{N}.$$

Therefore α preserves sums and products.

Finally, assume that m and n are natural numbers with $m > n$.
Then $m = n + u$ for some $u \in \mathbf{N}$. Hence

$$\alpha(m) = \alpha(n + u) = \alpha(n) + \alpha(u) = \alpha(n) + {}^{+}u.$$

Therefore

$$\alpha(m) + (-\alpha(n)) = {}^{+}u,$$

and so $\alpha(m) > \alpha(n)$. Therefore α is order-preserving. $\square$

In view of Theorem 46, we shall no longer maintain notational
distinction between a natural number and its corresponding positive
integer. Thus, for example, we shall use the symbol 1 to denote both
the natural number 1 and the positive integer ${}^{+}1$. This is standard
mathematical practice and should cause no confusion. We shall also
follow standard practice by using the symbol -1, to denote the integer
$-({}^{+}1)$ (which, of course, is the same as ${}^{-}1$), -2 to denote $-({}^{+}2)$, and
so on.

EXERCISES

1   Prove Theorem 45.

2   A set S of elements of an ordered integral domain is said to be *well-ordered* iff for each nonempty subset T of S there exists an element $l \in T$ such that $l \leq x$ for every $x \in T$. Prove that the set $P = \{{}^{+}n : n \in \mathbf{N}\}$ is well-ordered.

3   Let $(D; +, \cdot; D_p)$ be an ordered integral domain with unity element u, and let P be the set of positive integers. Define $1u = u$, $2u = u + u, \ldots, (n + 1)u = nu + u, \ldots$. Prove that if D_p is well-ordered, then $D_p = \{nu : n \in P\}$ and $D = \{mu : m \in Z\}$.

4   Prove that the ordered integral domains $(D; +, \cdot; D_p)$ and $(D'; \oplus, \odot; D'_p)$ are isomorphic if D_p and D'_p are both well-ordered. Therefore, in view of Exercise 2, there is one and essentially only one ordered integral domain whose set of positive elements is well-ordered.

The Rational Numbers

A_{10} The ordered integral domain of integers is not a *field*; that is, there are nonzero integers which do not have multiplicative inverses. For example, if $x \in \mathbf{Z}$ and $2x = 1$, then $0 < 2x < 2$, whence $2 \cdot 0 < 2x < 2 \cdot 1$, and so $0 < x < 1$. This implies that $1 < x + 1 < 2$. Since $2x = 1$, it follows that $x \in P$. Hence $(x + 1) \in P$. This is a contradiction of Exercise 4, p. 16. Hence $2x \neq 1$ for every $x \in \mathbf{Z}$. Therefore 2 has no multiplicative inverse.

A_{12} Our goal, then, is to manufacture from the elements of $\mathbf{Z}$ an *ordered field* containing a copy of the ordered integral domain of integers. The manufacturing process is similar to that employed in the construction of the integers: we shall form certain equivalence classes of ordered pairs of integers. The equivalence relation employed is devised from the point of view of causing the ordered pair of integers (a, b) to behave in the way we have been led to believe the fraction a/b ought to behave.

The following definition formalizes a quality of sameness for such ordered pairs of integers as (5,2), (10,4), and $(-15, -6)$.

47   DEFINITION

Let $T = \{(x, y) \in \mathbf{Z} \times \mathbf{Z} : y \neq 0\}$. If (p, q) and (r, s) are members of T, we shall say that (p, q) is *equivalent* to (r, s), and write "$(p, q) \ominus (r, s)$," iff $ps = qr$.

48   THEOREM

The relation $\ominus$ is an equivalence relation on the set T.

Proof

Since $pq = qp$ for all p and q in $\mathbf{Z}$ it follows that $(p, q) \ominus (p, q)$ for all $(p, q) \in T$. If $(p, q) \ominus (r, s)$, then $ps = qr$, so $rq = sp$. Therefore $(r, s) \ominus (p, q)$. If $(p, q) \ominus (r, s)$ and $(r, s) \ominus (t, u)$, then $ps = qr$ and $ru = st$. Therefore

$$(ps)u = (qr)u = q(ru).$$

But $ru = st$, so $(ps)u = q(st)$, from which it follows that $(pu)s = (qt)s$. Now $(r, s) \in T$, and so $s \neq 0$. Since $(\mathbf{Z}; +, \cdot)$ is an integral domain, it follows that $pu = qt$. Therefore $(p, q) \ominus (t, u)$. $\square$

49   DEFINITION

The set $\mathbf{Q}$ of *rational numbers* is the set of all $\ominus$-equivalence classes of T. That is, x is a rational number iff $x = [(p, q)]$ for some $(p, q) \in T$. The rational number *zero*, denoted by $0^{\bullet}$, is the equivalence class $[(0, 1)]$. The rational number *one*, denoted by $1^{\bullet}$, is the equivalence class $[(1, 1)]$. In general, for each $n \in \mathbf{Z}$, the rational number $n^{\bullet}$ is the equivalence class $[(n, 1)]$.

For the sake of avoiding tangles of parentheses and brackets, we shall again adopt the abbreviated notation $[a, b]$ for the $\ominus$-equivalence class containing the ordered pair (a, b).

50   DEFINITION

Given rational numbers x and y, let p, q, r, and s be integers such that $x = [p, q]$, $y = [r, s]$. (Note that neither q nor s can be 0.) We define the *sum* of x and y, denoted by $x + y$, by $x + y = [(ps + qr, qs)]$. We define the *product* of x and y, denoted by $x \cdot y$ or xy, by $x \cdot y = [pr, qs]$. (Since neither q nor s can be 0, it follows that qs is not 0. Hence $x + y$ and $x \cdot y$ are both rational numbers.)

51   LEMMA

The operations $+$ and $\cdot$ are well-defined on set $\mathbf{Q}$. That is, if $(a, b) \ominus (p, q)$ and $(c, d) \ominus (r, s)$, then $(ad + bc, bd) \ominus (ps + qr, qs)$ and $(ac, bd) \ominus (pr, qs)$.

Proof

Since $(a, b) \ominus (p, q)$ and $(c, d) \ominus (r, s)$, it follows that $aq = bp$ and that $cs = dr$. Therefore

$$(ad + bc)(qs) = (ad)(qs) + (bc)(qs)$$
$$= (aq)(ds) + (cs)(bq)$$
$$= (bp)(ds) + (dr)(bq)$$
$$= (bd)(ps) + (bd)(qr)$$
$$= (bd)(ps + qr),$$

and so $(ad + bc, bd) \ominus (ps + qr, qs)$.
Also

$$(ac)(qs) = (aq)(cs)$$
$$= (bp)(dr)$$
$$= (bd)(pr),$$

and so $(ac, bd) \ominus (pr, qs)$. □

EXERCISES

1 ▷ Let $(a, b) \in T$. Prove that $[a, b] = 0^\bullet$ if and only if $a = 0$.

2 Formulate definitions for the *difference* and *quotient* of two rational numbers. Show that these operations are well-defined on **Q**. (Such definitions become available "free of charge" when we have proved that $(\mathbf{Q}; +, \cdot)$ is a field. In the meantime, definitions *can* be given directly in terms of ordered pairs of integers.)

3 Using the definition formulated in Exercise 2, prove that if x and y are in **Q** and if $y \neq 0^\bullet$, then $(x \div y) = x \cdot (1^\bullet \div y)$.

4 Using the definition formulated in Exercise 2, prove that if x, y, z and w are in **Q**, and if y, z, $w = 0^\bullet$, then

$$(x \div y) \div (z \div w) = (x \div y) \cdot (w \div z)$$

The Rationals as an Ordered Field

Many of the theorems in this article are easy consequences of definitions and the fact that $(\mathbf{Z}; +, \cdot; P)$ is an ordered integral domain. The reader will be asked to write proofs of these theorems as exercises.

52   THEOREM   Commutative Laws

For every $x \in \mathbf{Q}$ and $y \in \mathbf{Q}$,

$$x + y = y + x,$$

and

$$x \cdot y = y \cdot x.$$

53   THEOREM   Associative Laws

For every x, y, and z in $\mathbf{Q}$, $(x + y) + z = x + (y + z)$, and $(xy)z = x(yz)$.

54   LEMMA

If p, q, r are in $\mathbf{Z}$ and neither q nor r is 0, then $[pr, qr] = [p, q]$.

55   THEOREM   Distributive Law of Multiplication over Addition

For every x, y, and z in $\mathbf{Q}$, $x(y + z) = xy + xz$.

56   THEOREM

For every $x \in \mathbf{Q}$, $x \cdot 1^{\bullet} = x$.

57   THEOREM

For every $x \in \mathbf{Q}$, $x + 0^{\bullet} = x$.

58   THEOREM

If $x \in \mathbf{Q}$, then there exists $y \in \mathbf{Q}$ such that $x + y = 0^{\bullet}$. Specifically, if $x = [p, q]$, then $x + [-p, q] = 0^{\bullet}$.

59   THEOREM

If $x \in \mathbf{Q}$ and $x \neq 0^{\bullet}$, then there exists $y \in \mathbf{Q}$ such that $xy = 1^{\bullet}$. Specifically, if $x = [p, q]$, $p \neq 0$, then $x \cdot [q, p] = 1^{\bullet}$.

The next lemma is needed to pave the way for the definition of the set of positive rational numbers.

60   LEMMA

If a and b are integers such that $ab > 0$, and if $(p, q) \in T$ and $(p, q) \ominus (a, b)$, then $pq > 0$.

Proof

Since $(p, q) \ominus (a, b)$, we have $pb = aq$. Since the integers form an ordered integral domain and $ab > 0$, either $a > 0$ and $b > 0$ or $a < 0$ and $b < 0$.

Now $q \neq 0$ because $(p, q) \in T$. Also $p = 0$ implies $aq = 0$, which implies $a = 0$ or $q = 0$, which implies $ab = 0$ or $q = 0$. Since $ab > 0$ and $q \neq 0$, it follows that $p \neq 0$.

Assume $p < 0$ and $q > 0$. Then if $a > 0$ and $b > 0$, we have $pb < 0$ and $aq > 0$. This contradicts $pb = aq$. If $a < 0$ and $b < 0$, then $pb > 0$ and $aq < 0$, again contradicting $pb = aq$.

Similarly, the assumption that $p > 0$ and $q < 0$ leads to a contradiction.

Therefore, either $p > 0$ and $q > 0$ or $p < 0$ and $q < 0$. In either case, $pq > 0$.   □

61   THEOREM

A$_{12}$
S$_{16}$
A$_{13}$
A$_{14}$

Let $P^\bullet = \{[a, b] \in \mathbf{Q} : ab > 0\}$. Then $(\mathbf{Q}; +, \cdot; P^\bullet)$ is an *ordered field*. Furthermore, there exists a *one-to-one, order-preserving* mapping of $\mathbf{Z}$ into $\mathbf{Q}$ that also *preserves sums and products* (that is, the rational numbers system contains a *copy* of $(\mathbf{Z}; +, \cdot; P)$).

Proof

Theorems 52, 53, 55, 56, 57, 58, and 59 imply that $(\mathbf{Q}; +, \cdot)$ is a field.

Lemma 60 asserts that $P^\bullet$ is well-defined with respect to the $\ominus$-equivalence classes.

Assume that $[a, b] \in P^\bullet$ and $[c, d] \in P^\bullet$. Then $[a, b] + [c, d] = [ad + bc, bd]$, and $bd(ad + bc) = abd^2 + cdb^2$. Now $ab > 0$, $cd > 0$, $b^2 > 0$ and $d^2 > 0$. Hence $bd(ad + bc) > 0$, and so $([a, b] + [c, d]) \in P^\bullet$. Also $[a, b] \cdot [c, d] = [ac, bd]$, and $(ac) \cdot (bd) = (ab)(cd) > 0$. Therefore $([a, b] \cdot [c, d]) \in P^\bullet$.

Let $[a, b] \in \mathbf{Q}$. Then $b \neq 0$. Now $ab = 0$ if and only if $a = 0$, and $a = 0$ if and only if $[a, b] = 0^\bullet$ (Exercise 1, p. 32). Moreover, $ab > 0$ if and only if $[a, b] \in P^\bullet$. Finally, $-(ab) > 0$ if and only if $(-a)b > 0$, and $(-a)b > 0$ if and only if $[-a, b] = -[a, b] \in P^\bullet$. Since $(\mathbf{Z}; +, \cdot; P)$ is an ordered integral domain, exactly one of $ab = 0$, $ab > 0$, or $-(ab) > 0$ is true. Hence exactly one of $[a, b] = 0^\bullet$, $[a, b] \in P^\bullet$, or $-[a, b] \in P^\bullet$ is true. Therefore $(\mathbf{Q}; +, \cdot; P^\bullet)$ is an ordered field.

For each $x \in \mathbf{Z}$, let $\beta(x) = [x, 1]$. If $[x_1, 1] = [x_2, 1]$ for some x_1 and x_2 in $\mathbf{Z}$ then $x_1 \cdot 1 = x_2 \cdot 1$, so $x_1 = x_2$. Hence β is one-to-one.

Assume that x_1 and x_2 are integers with $x_1 < x_2$. Then $[x_2, 1] + (-[x_1, 1]) = [x_2, 1] + [-x_1, 1] = [x_2 - x_1, 1]$, and $(x_2 - x_1) \cdot 1 = x_2 - x_1 > 0$. Therefore $[x_1, 1] < [x_2, 1]$, so $\beta(x_1) < \beta(x_2)$. Therefore β is order-preserving.

Let x_1 and x_2 be integers. Then $\beta(x_1 + x_2) = [x_1 + x_2, 1] = [x_1, 1] + [x_2, 1] = \beta(x_1) + \beta(x_2)$, and $\beta(x_1 x_2) = [x_1 x_2, 1] = [x_1, 1] \cdot [x_2, 1] = \beta(x_1) \cdot \beta(x_2)$. Therefore β preserves sums and products. $\square$

In view of Theorem 61, we shall no longer go out of our way to maintain the distinction between an integer n and the corresponding rational number $[n, 1]$.

Two important properties of the ordered field of rational numbers are stated in the following theorems.

62   THEOREM   Density of the Rationals in Themselves

If x and y are positive rational numbers, then there exists a positive number t such that $x < t < y$.

Proof

$2y = y + y < x + y < x + x = 2x$. Hence $y < \frac{1}{2}(x + y) < x$, so that $t = \frac{1}{2}(x + y)$ does the trick. $\square$

63   THEOREM   Archimedean Order of the Rationals

If x and y are positive rational numbers, then there exists a positive integer n such that $nx > y$.

Proof

Since $x \in P^{\bullet}$ and $y \in P^{\bullet}$, there exist positive integers p, q, r, and s such that $x = [p, q]$ and $y = [r, s]$. Then $ps \geq 1$, so that $2ps \geq 2 > 1$.

Therefore $2psqr > qr$, and so $(2qr)(ps) > qr$. Hence $[2qr, 1] \cdot [p, q] > [r, s]$, because $[2qr, 1][p, q] - [r, s] = [(2qr) \cdot (ps) - qr, qs]$, and $((2qr)(ps) - qr)(qs) > 0$ because $(2qr)(p) > qr, q > 0$, and $s > 0$. Therefore $(2qr)x > y$. Setting $n = 2qr$ then does the trick. $\square$

EXERCISES

1   Prove Theorem 52.

2   Prove Theorem 53.

3   Prove Lemma 54.

4   Prove Theorem 55.

5   Prove Theorem 56.

6   Prove Theorem 57.

7   Prove Theorem 58.

8   Prove Theorem 59.

9   ▷ Since $(\mathbf{Q}; +, \cdot; P^*)$ is an ordered field, the standard notion of *absolute value* of an element of $\mathbf{Q}$ is available. Specifically for each $x \in \mathbf{Q}$,

$$|x| = \begin{cases} x & \text{if} \quad x \geq 0, \\ -x & \text{if} \quad x < 0. \end{cases}$$

Prove that for each $x \in \mathbf{Q}$ and each $y \in \mathbf{Q}$, $|x + y| \leq |x| + |y|$.

10   ▷ Prove that there is no rational number r such that $r^2 = 2$.

11   Prove that if $p, q \in \mathbf{Z}$ and $q \neq 0$, then

$$[p, 1] \div [q, 1] = [p, q].$$

12   Prove that if $(F; +, \cdot)$ is a field containing a copy of the integral domain $(\mathbf{Z}; +, \cdot)$, then $(F; +, \cdot)$ also contains a copy[†] of the rational number field $(\mathbf{Q}; +, \cdot)$.

The Real Numbers

Many examples can be given to illustrate the inadequacy of the rational number system for the purposes of algebra, geometry, and analysis. Some typical examples: Not all rational numbers have rational square roots. There is no rational number that gives either the circumference or the area of a circle of unit radius. The sequence of rational numbers generated by $(1 + 1/n)^n$, $n \in \mathbf{N}$, has no rational limit.

There is, of course, a common remedy for all of these problems. That remedy is to extend the rational number system by means of a device called a *cut*, which was introduced by Dedekind in 1872. In effecting this remedy, the only properties of the rationals that we shall use are those stated in Theorems 61, 62, and 63.

The definition of cut that we shall employ here is actually a slight modification of that originally given by Dedekind. According to our

---

† "Copy" as used here means "isomorphic image."

definition, a cut is a single set, while Dedekind's definition declared
S₆ that a cut is determined by a set and its *complement*. The two definitions
are equivalent, but it is felt that the former is conceptually more
simple.†

The reader may find it helpful to keep in mind that eventually a
real number will be defined to be a cut.

64   DEFINITION

A subset A of $\mathbf{Q}$ is said to be a *cut* iff

[1] $A \neq \emptyset$ and $A \neq \mathbf{Q}$;
[2] if $a \in A$, $b \in \mathbf{Q}$, and $b < a$, then $b \in A$; and
[3] if $a \in A$, then there exists $c \in A$ such that $c > a$.

Cuts *do* exist. Indeed, there exists one corresponding to each
rational number q.

65   THEOREM

For each $q \in \mathbf{Q}$, let $C_q = \{x \in \mathbf{Q} : x < q\}$. Then C_q is a cut for each
$q \in \mathbf{Q}$.

Proof

Since $(q - 1) \in C_q$ and $(q + 1) \notin C_q$, it follows that $C_q \neq \emptyset$ and $C_q \neq \mathbf{Q}$.

If $a \in C_q$, then $a < q$. Hence if $b \in \mathbf{Q}$ and $b < a$, then $b < q$, so that
$b \in C_q$. Finally, if $a \in C_q$, then $a < q$. By Theorem 62 there exists $c \in \mathbf{Q}$
such that $a < c < q$. Then $c \in C_q$ and $c > a$. □

If it were the case that every cut is of the form C_q for some $q \in \mathbf{Q}$,
then we would have gained very little by introducing the concept of
cut.

66   THEOREM

Not every cut is of the form C_q for some $q \in \mathbf{Q}$. In particular, if
$B = \{x \in \mathbf{Q} : x \leq 0\} \cup \{x \in \mathbf{Q} : x > 0 \text{ and } x^2 < 2\}$, then B is a cut and
$B \neq C_q$ for every $q \in \mathbf{Q}$.

Proof

It is easy to see that $0 \in B$ and $2 \notin B$. Therefore $B \neq \emptyset$ and $B \neq \mathbf{Q}$.

† The interested reader is referred to G. H. Hardy, *A Course in Pure
Mathematics*, 10th edition (New York: Cambridge University Press, 1963),
for a discussion that follows Dedekind more closely.

Assume that $b \in B$, that $c \in Q$, and $c < b$. If $c \leq 0$ then $c \in B$ by definition of B. If $c > 0$, then $b > 0$, and so $b^2 < 2$. But

$$0 < c < b$$

implies

$$0 < c^2 < bc < b^2,$$

so that

$$c^2 < 2.$$

Hence

$$c \in B.$$

Assume that $b \in B$. If $b \leq 0$, then $1 > b$ and $1 \in B$. If $b > 0$, then $b^2 < 2$, so that $2 - b^2 > 0$. By the Archimedean order of the rationals, there exists $m \in P$ such that $m(2 - b^2) > 2b + 1$. Now

$$\left(b + \frac{1}{m}\right)^2 = b^2 + \frac{2b}{m} + \frac{1}{m^2} \leq b^2 + \frac{2b}{m} + \frac{1}{m} = b^2 + \frac{2b + 1}{m}.$$

But $m(2 - b^2) > 2b + 1$, so that

$$\frac{2b + 1}{m} < 2 - b^2.$$

Therefore

$$\left(b + \frac{1}{m}\right)^2 \leq b^2 + \frac{2b + 1}{m} < b^2 + (2 - b^2) = 2.$$

Hence

$$\left(b + \frac{1}{m}\right) \in B, \text{ and } \left(b + \frac{1}{m}\right) > b.$$

Therefore, B is a cut.

Note that the *complement in* Q of the rational cut C_q contains a smallest element, namely q itself. Therefore, if we show that the complement in Q of B contains no smallest element, it will follow that $B \neq C_q$ for every $q \in Q$.

Assume, then, that $c \in Q$ but $c \notin B$. Then $c > 0$ and $c^2 \geq 2$. But it follows from Exercise 10, p. 36, that $c^2 \neq 2$. Hence $c^2 > 2$, from which it follows that $(c^2 - 2) > 0$. By the Archimedean order of the rationals, there exists $n \in P$ such that $n(c^2 - 2) > 2c$. Then

$$\left(c - \frac{1}{n}\right)^2 = c^2 - \frac{2c}{n} + \frac{1}{n^2} > c^2 - \frac{2c}{n}.$$

But $n(c^2 - 2) > 2c$, so that

$$\frac{2c}{n} < c^2 - 2.$$

Therefore

$$\left(c - \frac{1}{n}\right)^2 > c^2 - \frac{2c}{n} > c^2 - (c^2 - 2) = 2.$$

Hence

$$\left(c - \frac{1}{n}\right) \notin B, \text{ and } \left(c - \frac{1}{n}\right) < c.$$

Therefore, the complement of B in $\mathbf{Q}$ contains no smallest element, and so $B \neq C_q$ for every $q \in \mathbf{Q}$. ☐

1 ▷ Let A be a cut. Prove that
   (a) if $a \subset A$ and $b \notin A$, then $a < b$; and,
   (b) if $b \notin A$, $c \in \mathbf{Q}$ and $c > b$, then $c \notin A$.

2 Prove that if A and B are cuts, then either $A \subset B$ or $B \subset A$.

3 Let p and q be rational numbers. Prove that $C_p \subset C_q$ if and only if $p \leq q$.

4 Let $A = \{x \in \mathbf{Q} : x \leq 0\} \cup \{x \in \mathbf{Q} : x > 0 \text{ and } x^2 < 5\}$. Prove that A is a cut, but that $A \neq C_q$ for every $q \in \mathbf{Q}$.

5 ▷ Prove that if A is a cut and r is a positive rational number, then there is an $a \in A$ such that $(a + r) \notin A$.

Addition of Cuts

Throughout the remainder of this book, the set of all cuts will be denoted by $\mathbf{K}$.

67 DEFINITION

For each $A \in \mathbf{K}$ and each $B \in \mathbf{K}$ we define $A + B$ to be the set

$$\{a + b : a \in A \text{ and } b \in B\}.$$

Our next theorem assures us that the sum of two cuts is always itself a cut.

68   THEOREM

If $A \in \mathbf{K}$ and $B \in \mathbf{K}$, then $(A + B) \in \mathbf{K}$.

Proof

[1] Since $A \in \mathbf{K}$, there exists a rational number $a_1 \in A$. Similarly, there exists a rational number $b_1 \in B$. Then the rational number $(a_1 + b_1)$ is a member of $A + B$ by Definition 67. Hence $(A + B) \neq \varnothing$. Also, there exists a rational number a_2 such that $a_2 \notin A$, and there exists a rational number b_2 such that $b_2 \notin B$. Since $a_2 \notin A$, it follows that $a_2 > a$ for every $a \in A$. Since $b_2 \notin B$, it follows that $b_2 > b$ for every $b \in B$. Therefore

$$a_2 + b_2 > a + b \qquad \text{for every} \quad a \in A, b \in B.$$

Hence

$$a_2 + b_2 > c \qquad \text{for every} \quad c \in (A + B),$$

and so

$$(a_2 + b_2) \notin (A + B).$$

Therefore $(A + B) \neq \mathbf{Q}$.

[2] Assume that $c \in (A + B)$, $d \in \mathbf{Q}$, and $d < c$. Since $c \in (A + B)$, there exist $a \in A$ and $b \in B$ such that $c = a + b$. Then $d < a + b$, and so $(d - a) < b$. Hence $(d - a) \in B$. But $d = a + (d - a)$, and $a \in A$, $(d - a) \in B$. Therefore $d \in (A + B)$.

[3] Assume that $c \in (A + B)$. Then there exist $a \in A$ and $b \in B$ such that $c = a + b$. Since A is a cut, there exists $d \in A$ such that $d > a$. Then $(d + b) \in (A + B)$, and $(d + b) > (a + b) = c$. $\square$

The definition of cut addition "preserves" rational sums in the following sense:

69   THEOREM

For each $p \in \mathbf{Q}$ and each $q \in \mathbf{Q}$,

$$C_p + C_q = C_{p+q}.$$

Proof

Assume that $x \in (C_p + C_q)$. Then $x = a + b$, where $a \in C_p$ and $b \in C_q$. Hence $a < p$ and $b < q$. Therefore $x = a + b < p + q$, whence $x \in C_{p+q}$.

Conversely, assume that $x \in C_{p+q}$. Then $x < (p + q)$. Let

$d = (p + q) - x$. Then $d > 0$ so
$$p - \tfrac{1}{2}d < p \quad \text{and} \quad q - \tfrac{1}{2}d < q.$$
Hence
$$(p - \tfrac{1}{2}d) \in C_p \quad \text{and} \quad (q - \tfrac{1}{2}d) \in C_q.$$
Also
$$(p - \tfrac{1}{2}d) + (q - \tfrac{1}{2}d) = p + q - d = x.$$
Therefore $x \in C_p + C_q$. ☐

There is an identity element for the operation of cut addition.

70   THEOREM

For every $A \in \mathbf{K}$, $A + C_0 = A$.

Proof

Assume that $x \in (A + C_0)$. Then $x = a + c$ where $a \in A$ and $c \in C_0$. Hence $c < 0$, so that $x = a + c < a$, Therefore $x \in A$.

Conversely, assume that $x \in A$. Then there exists $a \in A$ such that $a > x$. Then $d = x - a < 0$, so $d \in C_0$. Moreover
$$a + d = a + (x - a) = x,$$
so $x \in (A + C_0)$. ☐

Having established the existence of an additive identity, we now investigate the question of additive inverses.

71   DEFINITION

For each $A \in \mathbf{K}$ we define $- A$ to be the set
$$\{x \in \mathbf{Q} : x < -b \quad \text{for at least one} \quad b \notin A\}.$$

Happily, the negative of a cut turns out to be a cut.

72   THEOREM

For each $A \in \mathbf{K}$, $- A \in \mathbf{K}$.

Proof

[1] Since $A \in \mathbf{K}$, there is a rational number b such that $b \notin A$. Now $b + 1 > b$, so that
$$-(b + 1) < -b.$$
Therefore $-(b + 1) \in - A$, and so $- A \neq \varnothing$.

Since $A \in$ **K**, there is a rational number a such that $a \in A$. If it were the case that

$$-a < -b \qquad \text{for some} \quad b \notin A,$$

then $a > b$ for some $b \notin A$, which would imply that $a \notin A$. Therefore

$$-a \geq -b \qquad \text{for every} \quad b \notin A.$$

Therefore $(-a) \notin -A$; and so $-A \neq$ **Q**.

[2] Assume that $c \in -A$ and that $d < c$. Then $c < -b$ for some $b \notin A$. Hence $d < -b$ for some $b \notin A$, and so $d \in -A$.

[3] Assume that $c \in -A$. Then $c < -b$ for some $b \notin A$. Now

$$c < \tfrac{1}{2}(c + (-b)) < -b, \qquad \text{so} \qquad \tfrac{1}{2}(c + (-b)) \in -A. \quad \square$$

The cut $-A$ actually *is* the additive inverse of A.

73   THEOREM

For every $A \in$ **K**, $A + (-A) = C_0$.

Proof

Assume that $x \in (A + (-A))$. Then $x = a + b$ where $a \in A$ and $b \in -A$. Hence there exists a rational number c such that $c \notin A$ and $b < -c$. Then

$$x = a + b < a + (-c) < 0$$

because $a < c$ ($a \in A$, $c \notin A$). Hence $x \in C_0$.

Conversely, assume that $x \in C_0$. Then $x < 0$, and so $-\tfrac{1}{2}x > 0$. It follows from Exercise 5, p. 39, that there is an $a \in A$ such that $a + (-\tfrac{1}{2}x) = b \notin A$. Hence

$$x = a + (\tfrac{1}{2}x - b).$$

Now $a \in A$, and $(\tfrac{1}{2}x - b) < -b$, so that $(\tfrac{1}{2}x - b) \in -A$. Therefore $x \in (A + (-A))$. $\square$

The proofs of the next two theorems are left as exercises for the reader.

74   THEOREM

For every $A \in$ **K** and every $B \in$ **K**, $A + B = B + A$. For every $A \in$ **K**, every $B \in$ **K**, and every $C \in$ **K**, $(A + B) + C = A + (B + C)$.

75   THEOREM

For every $q \in \mathbf{Q}$, $-C_q = C_q$.

As usual, subtraction is defined as addition of the additive inverse.

76   DEFINITION

If $A \in \mathbf{K}$ and $B \in \mathbf{K}$, then $A - B$ is defined to be the cut $A + (-B)$.

EXERCISES

1   Prove Theorem 74.

2   Prove Theorem 75.

A_2 3   ▷ Verify that the system $(\mathbf{K}; +)$ is an *abelian group*.

4   Prove that if $A \in \mathbf{K}$ and $q \in \mathbf{Q}$, then the set

$$B - \{q \mid a : a \in A\}$$

is a cut, and

$$B = C_q + A.$$

Order in the Set **K**

As remarked in Exercise 3, above, the system $(\mathbf{K}; +)$ is an abelian group. Our goal is to construct an ordered field $(\mathbf{K}; +, \cdot; P)$, so that the next step might appear to be the statement of a definition of cut multiplication. Natural as this course of action seems, there are some rather nasty problems that arise. For example, the "natural" definition of $A \cdot B$ as the set $\{ab : a \in A \text{ and } b \in B\}$ simply will not do. Whatever our definition of $A \cdot B$ turns out to be, it is highly desirable to have, for example, $C_2 \cdot C_3 = C_6$; but the set $\{ab : a \in C_2 \text{ and } b \in C_3\}$ contains the rational number $(-4) \cdot (-5) = 20$, and $20 \notin C_6$.

We can avoid these difficulties by first defining an order relation $>$ on $\mathbf{K}$, then defining multiplication of cuts using the notion of order, and finally showing that the set of $\{A \in \mathbf{K} : A > C_0\}$ satisfies the axioms for the set of positive elements in an ordered field.

77   DEFINITION

We shall say that a cut A is a *positive* cut iff A contains at least one positive rational number. The set of all positive cuts will be denoted by

K_p. If A and B are cuts, then $A > B$ means that $(A - B) \in K_p$, and $A < B$ means that $B > A$.

The next theorem is an easy consequence of Definition 77, and its proof is left as an exercise.

78   THEOREM

If A is a cut, then $A > C_0$ if and only if $A \in K_p$. If $A \in K_p$ and $B \in K_p$, then $(A + B) \in K_p$.

The trichotomy law holds for our order relation on K.

79   THEOREM

For each $A \in K$, one and only one of the following statements is true:

$$A = C_0, \, A > C_0, \, -A > C_0.$$

Proof

[1] We shall show first that at least one of the statements is true. Assume that $A \in K$.

(a) If A contains a positive rational number, then $A \in K_p$, and so $A > C_0$.

(b) If A does not contain a positive rational number, then $x \le 0$ for every $x \in A$. But if $0 \in A$, then there exists $c \in A$ such that $c > 0$, a contradiction. Hence $0 \notin A$, and so $x < 0$ for every $x \in A$.

(i) Assume that there exists $q < 0$ such that $q \notin A$. Then $-q > 0$, and so $-q > \frac{1}{2}(-q) > 0$. Hence $\frac{1}{2}(-q) \in -A$, and since $\frac{1}{2}(-q) > 0$ we have $-A \in K_p$, whence $-A > C_0$.

(ii) If there is no $q < 0$ such that $q \notin A$, then $x \in A$ for every $x < 0$. Hence $x \in A$ if and only if $x < 0$, so $A = C_0$.

[2] We shall now show that at most one of the statements is true.

(a) Assume that $A = C_0$. Then $A = \{x \in Q : x < 0\}$. Hence A contains no positive rational number. Therefore $A \notin K_p$, and so $A \not> C_0$. Also $-A = -C_0 = C_{-0} = C_0 = A$, so that $-A \not> C_0$.

(b) Assume that $A > C_0$. Then A contains a positive rational number. Hence $A \ne C_0$, because C_0 contains no positive rational number. Suppose that $x \in -A$. Then there exists $b \notin A$ such that $x < -b$. Now $b > 0$, since $b \le 0$ would imply that $b \in A$ (remember A contains a positive element). Therefore $-b < 0$, and so $x < 0$. Hence

$x \in -A$ implies that $x < 0$. Therefore $-A$ contains no positive rational number. Hence $-A \notin \mathbf{K}_p$, and so $-A \not> C_0$.

(c) Assume that $-A > C_0$. Then $-A$ contains a positive rational number q. Since $q \in -A$ there exists $b \notin A$ such that $q < -b$. Since $q > 0$, it follows that $-b > 0$, and so $b < 0$. Now if $x \in A$, then $x < b$ (because $x \geq b$ would imply $x \notin A$), so that $x < b < 0$ for every $x \in A$. Therefore A contains no positive elements. Hence $A \not> C_0$. Furthermore, A does not contain all negative rational numbers ($b < 0$ and $b \notin A$), so $A \neq C_0$. $\square$

Since the system $(\mathbf{K}, +)$ is a group (Exercise 3, p. 43), we know on purely group-theoretic grounds that $-(-A) = A$ for every $A \in \mathbf{K}$. This fact is needed to prove our next theorem.

80 THEOREM

Let A be any cut. If $A > C_0$, then $-A < C_0$; and if $A < C_0$, then $-A > C_0$.

Proof

Assume $A > C_0$. Then $A \in \mathbf{K}_p$. Also

$$C_0 - (-A) = C_0 + (-(-A)) = C_0 + A = A,$$

and so $(C_0 - (-A)) \in \mathbf{K}_p$. Therefore $C_0 > -A$.

Assume $A < C_0$. Then $(C_0 - A) \in \mathbf{K}_p$. But

$$C_0 - A = C_0 + (-A) = -A.$$

Hence $-A \in \mathbf{K}_p$, and so $-A > C_0$. $\square$

One's natural suspicions concerning the nature of $<$ with respect to set inclusion are indeed well-founded.

81 THEOREM

Let A and B be cuts. Then $A < B$ if and only if $A \subset B$ and $A \neq B$.

Proof

Assume that $A \subset B$ and $A \neq B$. Then there is a rational number b_0 such that $b_0 \in B$ but $b_0 \notin A$. Since B is a cut, there are rational numbers b_1 and b_2 in B such that $b_0 < b_1 < b_2$. Now $-b_1 < -b_0$, and $b_0 \notin A$. Hence $-b_1 \in -A$. Since $b_2 > b_1$, $b_2 - b_1 > 0$. But $b_2 - b_1 = b_2 + (-b_1)$, and so $(b_2 - b_1) \in [B + (-A)] = B - A$. Therefore $(B - A) \in \mathbf{K}_p$. Hence $A < B$.

Conversely, assume that $A < B$. Then $B - A = [B + (-A)] \in \mathbf{K}_p$. Hence there is a positive rational number q such that $q \in [B + (-A)]$. This implies that there are rational numbers b and c with $b \in B$ and $c \in -A$ such that $q = b + c$.

Since $c \in -A$ there exists $d \notin A$ such that $c < -d$. Therefore $-c > d$. Now $b + c = q > 0$, so $b > -c > d$. Therefore $b \notin A$. Since $b \in B$ but $b \notin A$, it follows that $A \neq B$. Moreover, if $x \in A$, then $x < b$, so that $x \in B$. Hence $A \subset B$. □

The next definition is the standard definition of absolute value in an ordered field. It is stated here because we do not as yet *have* an ordered field of cuts.

82   DEFINITION

For each $A \in \mathbf{K}$ we define the *absolute value* of A, denoted by $|A|$, as follows:

$$|A| = \begin{cases} A & \text{if} \quad A \geq C_0, \\ -A & \text{if} \quad A < C_0. \end{cases}$$

EXERCISES

1   Prove that if $A \in \mathbf{K}$, $q \in \mathbf{Q}$, and $q \notin A$, then $A \leq C_q$.

2   Prove that if $A \in \mathbf{K}$ and $q \in \mathbf{Q}$, then $q \in A$ if and only if $C_q < A$.

3   ▷ Let p and q be rational numbers. Prove that $C_p < C_q$ if and only if $p < q$.

4   Prove Theorem 78.

5   ▷ Prove that $|A| \geq C_0$ for every $A \in \mathbf{K}$, and that $|A| = C_0$ if and only if $A = C_0$.

6   ▷ Prove that if B and C are positive cuts and r is a positive rational number such that $r \in (B + C)$, then there exist *positive* rational numbers b and c with $b \in B$ and $c \in C$ such that $r = b + c$.

The Ordered Field of Real Numbers

Having established an order relation on $\mathbf{K}$, we can now proceed to define multiplication of cuts. The strategy is to define multiplication first for positive cuts, and then to define the product of arbitrary cuts in terms of the product of their absolute values.

For a given positive cut A we shall denote by A_p the set of all positive elements of A. That is,

$$A_p = \{x \in A : x > 0\}.$$

83 THEOREM

If A and B are cuts such that $A > C_0$ and $B > C_0$ then the set

$$S = \{ab : a \in A_p \text{ and } b \in B_p\} \cup \{x \in \mathbf{Q} : x \le 0\}$$

is a cut. Specifically, $S \in \mathbf{K}_p$.

Proof

[1] It is clear that $0 \in S$, so $S \ne \varnothing$. Since $A \ne \mathbf{Q}$ and $B \ne \mathbf{Q}$, there exist positive rational numbers c and d such that $c \notin A$ and $d \notin B$. Then $a < c$ for every $a \in A$ and $b < d$ for every $b \in B$. Therefore $0 < ab < cd$ for every $a \in A_p$ and every $b \in B_p$. Hence $cd \notin S$, and so $S \ne \mathbf{Q}$.

[2] Assume that $c \in S$ and that $d < c$. If $d \le 0$, then $d \in S$ by definition. We therefore assume that $0 < d < c$. Then there are positive rational numbers a and b with $a \in A_p$ and $b \in B_p$ such that $c = ab$.

Then

$$0 < d < ab,$$

so

$$0 < \frac{d}{a} < b.$$

Hence

$$\frac{d}{a} \in B_p.$$

Therefore

$$d = a\left(\frac{d}{a}\right) \in S.$$

[3] Assume that $c \in S$. There are positive rational numbers a_0 and b_0 such that $a_0 \in A_p$ and $b_0 \in B_p$, since $A > C_0$ and $B > C_0$. Then $a_0 b_0 \in S$ and $a_0 b_0 > 0$. This proves that

(a) if S turns out to be a cut at all, then $S \in \mathbf{K}_p$; and

(b) if $c \le 0$, then $c < a_0 b_0 \in S$.

Assume that $c > 0$. Then there exist $a \in A_p$ and $b \in B_p$ such that $c = ab$. Since A and B are cuts, there exists $a_1 \in A_p$ such that $a_1 > a$, and there exists $b_1 \in B_p$ such that $b_1 > b$.

Then $c = ab < a_1 b_1 \in S$. Therefore S is a cut, and, as remarked above, since S contains at least one positive rational number, $S \in \mathbf{K}_p$. $\square$

We are now ready to define multiplication of cuts.

84   DEFINITION

For each $A \in \mathbf{K}$ and each $B \in \mathbf{K}$ we define AB as follows:
 [1] If $A > C_0$ and $B > C_0$, then

$$AB = \{ab : a \in A_p \text{ and } b \in B_p\} \cup \{x \in \mathbf{Q} : x \leq 0\}$$

 [2] If $A > C_0$ and $B < C_0$, or if $A < C_0$ and $B > C_0$, then

$$AB = -(|A| |B|).$$

 [3] If $A < C_0$ and $B < C_0$, then

$$AB = |A| |B|.$$

 [4] If $A = C_0$ or if $B = C_0$, then

$$AB = C_0.$$

The next theorem is an easy consequence of Definitions 82 and 84, and Theorems 72, 79, 80, and 83; its proof is left as an exercise.

85   THEOREM

If $A \in \mathbf{K}$ and $B \in \mathbf{K}$, then $AB \in \mathbf{K}$. If $A \in \mathbf{K}_p$ and $B \in \mathbf{K}_p$, then $AB \in \mathbf{K}_p$.

Note that Theorems 78, 79, and 85 tell us that *if* $(\mathbf{K}; +, \cdot)$ is in fact a field, then $(\mathbf{K}; +, \cdot; \mathbf{K}_p)$ is an ordered field.

86   THEOREM

If $A \in \mathbf{K}$ and $B \in \mathbf{K}$, then

$$A(-B) = (-A)B = -(AB).$$

Proof

If $A = C_0$ or $B = C_0$, then $A(-B) = C_0$, $(-A)B = C_0$, and $-(AB) = C_0$, and so the assertion of the theorem is true.
   Assume, then, that $A \neq C_0$ and $B \neq C_0$.
   [1] $A > C_0$ and $B > C_0$. Then $-B < C_0$, so

$$A(-B) = -(|A| \cdot |-B|) \qquad \text{D84}$$

$$= -[A \cdot (-(-B))] \qquad \text{D82}$$

$$= -(AB) \qquad \text{since } (\mathbf{K}; +) \text{ is a group.}$$

Also $-A < C_0$, so

$$(-A)B = -(|-A| \cdot |B|) = -(-(-A) \cdot B)$$
$$= -(A \cdot B).$$

[2] $A > C_0$ and $B < C_0$. Then $-A < C_0$, so

$$(-A)(B) = |-A| \cdot |B| \qquad \text{D84}$$
$$= (-(-A)) \cdot (-B) \qquad \text{D82}$$
$$= A \cdot (-B) \qquad \text{since } (\mathbf{K}, +) \text{ is a group.}$$

Also

$$AB = -(|A| \cdot |B|) \qquad \text{D84}$$
$$= -(A(-B)) \qquad \text{D82}$$

so

$$-(AB) = -[-(A(-B))]$$
$$= A(-B) \qquad \text{since } (\mathbf{K}; +) \text{ is a group.}$$

[3] $A < C_0$ and $B > C_0$. Then $-B < C_0$, so

$$A(-B) = |A| \cdot |-B| \qquad \text{D84}$$
$$= (-A) \cdot (-(-B)) \qquad \text{D82}$$
$$= (-A) \cdot B \qquad \text{since } (\mathbf{K}; +) \text{ is a group.}$$

Also

$$AB = -(|A| \cdot |B|) \qquad \text{D84}$$
$$= -((-A)B), \qquad \text{D82}$$

so

$$-(AB) = -[-((-A)B)]$$
$$= (-A)B \qquad \text{since } (\mathbf{K}; +) \text{ is a group.}$$

[4] $A < C_0$ and $B < C_0$. Then $-A > C_0$, so

$$(-A)B = -(|A| \cdot |B|) \qquad \text{D84}$$
$$= -((-A)(-B)) \qquad \text{D82}$$

Also

$$A(-B) = -(|A| |-B|) \qquad \text{D84}$$
$$= ((-A)(-B)) \qquad \text{D82.}$$

Finally

$$AB = |A| |B| \qquad \text{D84}$$
$$= (-A)(-B) \qquad \text{D82}$$

so that

$$-(AB) = -((-A)(-B)). \quad \square$$

87   THEOREM

For every $A \in \mathbf{K}$, every $B \in \mathbf{K}$, and every $C \in \mathbf{K}$,

$$AB = BA \quad \text{and} \quad (AB)C = A(BC).$$

Proof

Since multiplication is commutative in $\mathbf{Q}$, it follows from Definition 84 [1] that $AB = BA$ if $A > C_0$ and $B > C_0$. But AB is defined in terms of a product of positive cuts in parts [2] and [3] of Definition 84, so that $AB = BA$ in these cases also. The result is truly trivial if either A or B is C_0.

If $A > C_0$, $B > C_0$, and $C > C_0$, it follows easily from Definition 84 [1] and the fact that multiplication is associative in $\mathbf{Q}$ that $(AB)C = A(BC)$. The remaining cases are then routinely handled by making use of Theorem 86. For example, if $A < C_0$, $B > C_0$, and $C > C_0$, then $-A > C_0$, and so

$$((-A)B)C = (-A)(BC)$$

since all three factors are positive.

But $(-A)B = -(AB)$ by Theorem 86, and $(-A)(BC) = -(A(BC))$, also by Theorem 86. Hence

$$(-(AB))C = -(A(BC)).$$

But, again by Theorem 86,

$$(-(AB))C = -((AB)C),$$

so that

$$-((AB)C) = -(A(BC)).$$

Therefore, since $(\mathbf{K}; +)$ is a group,

$$(AB)C = A(BC).$$

The proof in the remaining cases is left as an exercise. □

The distributive law of multiplication over addition turns out to have a fairly involved proof. Fortunately, the way has been prepared in the exercises on p. 46.

88   THEOREM

For every $A \in \mathbf{K}$, every $B \in \mathbf{K}$, and every $C \in \mathbf{K}$,

$$A(B + C) = AB + AC.$$

Proof

If $A = C_0$, we then have

$$A(B + C) = C_0(B + C) = C_0 = C_0 + C_0$$
$$= C_0 \cdot B + C_0 \cdot C = AB + AC.$$

If $B = C_0$, then

$$A(B + C) = A(C_0 + C) = AC = C_0 + AC$$
$$= A \cdot C_0 + AC = AB + AC.$$

If $C = C_0$, then

$$A(B + C) = A(B + C_0) = AB = AB + C_0$$
$$= AB + A \cdot C_0$$
$$= AB + AC.$$

Let us now assume that $A \neq C_0$, $B \neq C_0$, and $C \neq C_0$.

[1] $A > C_0$, $B > C_0$, and $C > C_0$. In this case $A(B + C)$ and $AB + AC$ are both positive cuts. Hence it suffices to show that

$$(A(B + C))_p = (AB + AC)_p.$$

If $q > 0$ and $q \in (A(B + C))$, then $q = ar$ where $a \in A$ and $r \in (B + C)$. But then (see Exercise 6, p. 46),

$$r = b + c \qquad \text{where} \quad b \in B_p, c \in C_p.$$

Hence

$$q = a(b + c) = (ab + ac) \in (AB + AC).$$

Conversely, assume $q > 0$ and $q \in (AB + AC)$. Applying Exercise 6, p. 46 we have $q = d + e$ where $d \in (AB)_p$ and $e \in (AC)_p$. Hence there are positive rational numbers a_1, a_2, b, and c with $a_1 \in A_p$, $a_2 \in A_p$, $b \in B_p$, and $c \in C_p$, such that $d = a_1 b$ and $e = a_2 c$. If $a_1 \leq a_2$, then

$$q = d + e = a_1 b + a_2 c \leq a_2 b + a_2 c = a_2(b + c) \in A(B + C),$$

while if $a_2 < a_1$, then

$$q = d + e = a_1 b + a_2 c < a_1 b + a_1 c = a_1(b + c) \in A(B + C).$$

[2] $A > C_0, B < C_0$, and $C > C_0$. Assume $B + C = C_0$. Then $C = -B$, so that

$$A(B + C) = A \cdot C_0 = C_0 = AB + (-AB)$$
$$= AB + A(-B) \qquad\qquad \text{T86}$$
$$= AB + AC.$$

Assume $B + C > C_0$. Then

$$AC = A(C_0 + C) = A[(-B + B) + C]$$
$$= A[-B + (B + C)]$$
$$= A(-B) + A(B + C) \qquad\qquad [1]\ (-B > C_0)$$
$$= -(AB) + A(B + C) \qquad\qquad \text{T86.}$$

Hence

$$AC + AB = A(B + C).$$

Assume $B + C < C_0$. Then

$$-(AB) = A(-B) \qquad\qquad \text{T86}$$
$$= A(C_0 + (-B))$$
$$= A[(C + (-C)) + (-B)]$$
$$= A[C + ((-C) + (-B))]$$
$$= A[C + (-(C + B))] \qquad\qquad \text{since } (\mathbf{K}\,;\,+) \text{ is a group}$$
$$= A[C + (-(B + C))]$$
$$= AC + A(-(B + C)) \qquad\qquad [1]$$
$$= AC + [-(A(B + C))] \qquad\qquad \text{T86 .}$$

Hence

$$A(B + C) = AC + AB = AB + AC.$$

[3] $A > C_0, B > C_0$, and $C < C_0$. Proceed as in [2], interchanging the roles of B and C.

[4] $A > C_0$, $B < C_0$, and $C < C_0$.
Then

$$-(A(B + C)) = A \cdot (-(B + C)) \qquad\qquad \text{T86}$$
$$= A \cdot ((-B) + (-C)) \qquad\qquad \text{since } (\mathbf{K}\,;\,+) \text{ is a group}$$
$$= A(-B) + A(-C) \qquad\qquad [1]$$
$$= -(AB) + (-(AC)) \qquad\qquad \text{T86}$$
$$= -(AB + AC) \qquad\qquad \text{since } (\mathbf{K}\,;\,+) \text{ is a group.}$$

Therefore

$$A(B + C) = AB + AC.$$

[5] $A < C_0$. Then

$$-(A(B + C)) = (-A)(B + C) \qquad \text{T86}$$
$$= (-A)B + (-A)C \qquad \text{[1]}$$
$$= -(AB) + (-(AC)) \qquad \text{T86}$$
$$= -(AB + AC).$$

Therefore

$$A(B + C) = AB + AC. \quad \square$$

Not surprisingly, the cut C_1 is the multiplicative identity.

89   THEOREM

For every $A \in \mathbf{K}$, $AC_1 = A$.

Proof

[1] If $A = C_0$, then

$$AC_1 = C_0 C_1 = C_0 = A \qquad \text{D84.}$$

[2] Assume $A > C_0$.

(a) Assume $z \in AC_1$. If $z \le 0$, then $z \in A$. If $z > 0$, then there are positive rational numbers a and c with $a \in A_p$ and $c \in (C_1)_p$ such that $z = ac$.

Now $0 < c < 1$ and $a > 0$, so $0 < ac < a$. Therefore $z \in A$.

(b) Conversely, assume $z \in A$. If $z \le 0$, then $z \in AC_1$. If $z > 0$, then there is a rational number $a \in A$ such that $a > z$. Then

$$0 < \frac{z}{a} < 1,$$

so that

$$\left(\frac{z}{a}\right) \in (C_1)_p.$$

Therefore

$$z = a\left(\frac{z}{a}\right) \in AC_1.$$

[3] Assume $A < C_0$. Then $-A > C_0$, so

$$AC_1 = -[(-A)C_1] \qquad \text{T86}$$
$$= -(-A) \qquad \text{[2]}$$
$$= A, \qquad \qquad \text{since } (\mathbf{K}; +) \text{ is a group.} \quad \square$$

Having produced a multiplicative identity, we next go to work on the problem of multiplicative inverses.

90   DEFINITION

For each $A \in \mathbf{K}$ with $A > C_0$, we define A^{-1} to be the set

$$\left\{ x \in \mathbf{Q} : x < \frac{1}{b} \text{ for some } b \notin A \right\}.$$

91   THEOREM

For each $A \in \mathbf{K}$ with $A > C_0$, $A^{-1} \in \mathbf{K}$ and $A^{-1} > C_0$.

Proof

[1] Since A is a cut, there exists a rational number b such that $b \notin A$. Since $A > C_0$, $b > 0$. Therefore $2b > b$, and so

$$\frac{1}{2b} < \frac{1}{b},$$

whence

$$\left(\frac{1}{2b} \right) \in A^{-1}.$$

Hence $A^{-1} \neq \varnothing$. Also

$$\frac{1}{2b} > 0,$$

so that *if* A^{-1} is a cut at all, $A^{-1} > C_0$.

Since A is a positive cut, there is a positive rational number a such that $a \in A$. Then $b > a$ for every $b \notin A$. Hence

$$\frac{1}{b} < \frac{1}{a}$$

for every $b \notin A$, and so

$$\left(\frac{1}{a} \right) \notin A^{-1}.$$

Therefore $A^{-1} \neq \mathbf{Q}$.

[2] Assume that $p \in A^{-1}$ and $q < p$. Then

$$p < \frac{1}{b}$$

for some $b \notin A$. Hence

$$q < \frac{1}{b},$$

and so $q \in A^{-1}$.

[3] Assume that $p \in A^{-1}$. Then

$$p < \frac{1}{b} \quad \text{for some} \quad b \notin A.$$

Now there is a rational number q such that

$$p < q < \frac{1}{b},$$

and so $q \in A^{-1}$. $\square$

92 DEFINITION

For each $A \in \mathbf{K}$ with $A < C_0$, we define A^{-1} to be the cut

$$-((-A)^{-1}).$$

Note that it follows from Theorems 91, 80, and 72 that $-((-A)^{-1})$ actually *is* cut when $A < C_0$.

93 THEOREM

For each $A \in \mathbf{K}$ with $A \neq C_0$, $AA^{-1} = C_1$.
Proof

[1] Assume that $A > C_0$.

Assume that $z \in AA^{-1}$. If $z \leq 0$, then $z \in C_1$. If $z > 0$, then there exist $a \in A_p$ and $q \in A_p^{-1}$ such that $z = aq$. Hence there exists $b \notin A$ such that

$$0 < q < \frac{1}{b}.$$

Therefore

$$0 < z = aq < a\frac{1}{b} < 1$$

because $a < b(a \in A, b \notin A)$. Hence $z \in C_1$. Conversely, assume that $z \in C_1$. If $z \leq 0$, then $z \in AA^{-1}$. If $z > 0$, then $z < 1$, so $(1 - z) > 0$.

Since $A > C_0$, there exists $a \in A_p$. Now $a(1 - z) > 0$, so by Exercise 5, p. 39 there exists $a_1 \in A_p$ such that $[a_1 + a(1 - z)] \notin A$. Let $b = a_1 + a(1 - z)$. Then, since $b \notin A$, $b > 0$. Let a_2 be the larger of a and a_1. Then $a_2 \geq a > 0$, $a_2 \geq a_1$, and $a_2 \in A_p$.

Furthermore

$$0 < a < b \qquad \text{(because } a \in A, b \notin A\text{)},$$

$$0 < a_2 < b \qquad \text{(same reason as above)},$$

and $1 - z > 0$, so

$$0 < b - a_2 \leq b - a_1 = a(1 - z) < b(1 - z).$$

Therefore $(b - a_2) + zb < b(1 - z) + zb = b$, so $-a_2 + zb < 0$, whence $zb < a_2$. Hence

$$\frac{z}{a_2} < \frac{1}{b},$$

so

$$\frac{z}{a_2} \in A_p^{-1}.$$

Therefore

$$z = a_2 \left(\frac{z}{a_2} \right) \in AA^{-1}.$$

It follows that $AA^{-1} = C_1$.

[2] Assume that $A < C_0$. Then $-A > C_0$ and $A^{-1} = -((-A)^{-1})$, so that

$$AA^{-1} = A \cdot (-(-A)^{-1})$$

$$= (-A) \cdot (-A)^{-1} \qquad \text{T86}$$

$$= C_1 \qquad\qquad [1]. \qquad \square$$

Note that cut multiplication "preserves" rational products in the following sense:

94   THEOREM

For each $p \in \mathbf{Q}$ and each $q \in \mathbf{Q}$, $C_p C_q = C_{pq}$.

Proof

[1] Assume $p > 0$ and $q > 0$. Suppose $z \in C_p C_q$. If $z \leq 0$, then $z \in C_{pq}$. If $z > 0$, then there are positive rational numbers a and b with $a \in C_p$ and $b \in C_q$ such that $z = ab$.

Now $0 < a < p$ and $0 < b < q$, so $0 < ab < pq$. Therefore $z = ab \in C_{pq}$.

Suppose $z \in C_{pq}$. If $z \leq 0$, then $z \in C_p C_q$.

If $0 < z < pq$, then there is a rational number r such that $z < r < pq$. Hence

$$0 < \frac{r}{p} < q, \qquad \text{so} \qquad \frac{r}{p} \in C_q.$$

Also

$$0 < \frac{z}{r} < 1, \qquad \text{so} \qquad 0 < \frac{zp}{r} < p,$$

whence

$$\frac{zp}{r} \in C_p.$$

Therefore $z = (zp/r)(r/p) \in C_p C_q$. Hence $C_p C_q - C_{pq}$.

[2] Assume $p < 0$, $q > 0$. Then

$$
\begin{aligned}
C_p C_q &= -(|C_p| |C_q|) = -(-C_p \cdot C_q) \\
&= -(C_{-p} \cdot C_q) = -C_{-pq} \qquad [1] \\
&= C_{pq}.
\end{aligned}
$$

[3] Assume $p > 0$, $q < 0$. Then

$$
\begin{aligned}
C_p \cdot C_q &= -(|C_p| |C_q|) = -(C_p \cdot (-C_q)) \\
&= -(C_p C_{-q}) = -C_{-pq} \\
&= C_{pq}.
\end{aligned}
$$

[4] Assume $p < 0$, $q < 0$. Then

$$
\begin{aligned}
C_p C_q &= |C_p| |C_q| = (-C_p)(-C_q) = C_{-p} \cdot C_{-q} \\
&= C_{pq}.
\end{aligned}
$$

[5] Assume $p = 0$ or $q = 0$. Then either $C_p = C_0$ or $C_q = C_0$, so that

$$C_p \cdot C_q = C_0.$$

But $pq = 0$ also, so

$$C_p \cdot C_q = C_{pq}. \quad \square$$

Our next theorem is the inevitable outcome of the struggle that began with Definition 64. Its proof—more accurately, the verification that it is true—is left as an exercise.

95   THEOREM

A_{12} The system $(\mathbf{K}; +, \cdot ; \mathbf{K}_p)$ is an *ordered field* (which we shall refer to hereafter as the *real number field*).

S_{16} Furthermore, there exists a *one-to-one, order-preserving mapping*
A_{13} of $\mathbf{Q}$ into $\mathbf{K}$ that also *preserves sums and products* (that is, the real
A_{14} number field contains a *copy* of $(\mathbf{Q}; +, \cdot ; P^{\bullet})$).

Two of the important properties of the rational number field are shared by the real number field.

96   THEOREM   Density of the Rationals in the Reals

If $A \in \mathbf{K}$, $B \in \mathbf{K}$, and $A < B$, then there exists $q \in \mathbf{Q}$ such that

$$A < C_q < B.$$

Proof

Since $A < B$, there exists a rational number r such that $r \in B$ but $r \notin A$ (Theorem 81). Now $r \in B$ implies that there are rational numbers q and s in B such that $r < q < s$. Now if $x \in A$, then $x < r$ because $r \notin A$. Hence $x < q$, so $x \in C_q$. Also $r \in C_q$ but $r \notin A$, so $A \neq C_q$. It follows from Theorem 81 that $A < C_q$.

If $x \in C_q$ then $x < q$. But $q \in B$, and so $x \in B$. Therefore $C_q \subset B$. Also $s \in B$ but $s \notin C_q$, so $C_q \neq B$. Therefore $C_q < B$. $\square$

97   THEOREM   Archimedean Order of the Reals

If $A \in \mathbf{K}_p$ and $B \in \mathbf{K}_p$ then there exists a positive integer n such that $C_n \cdot A > B$.

Proof

Since $A > C_0$, there exists a rational number q such that

$$C_0 < C_q < A.$$

It follows from Exercise 3, p. 46 that $q > 0$. Moreover, there is a rational number r such that $r \notin B$. Since $B > C_0, r > 0$. Let $t = r + 1$.

If $x \in B$, then $x < r$ because $r \notin B$. Hence $x < t$. Therefore $B \subset C_t$. Furthermore $r \in C_t$, but $r \notin B$. Hence $C_t \neq B$, whence $B < C_t$.

By the Archimedean order of the rationals, there is a positive integer n such that $nq > t$. It then follows (Exercise 3, p. 46) that $C_{nq} > C_t$. But $C_{nq} = C_n C_q$, so $C_n C_q > C_t$. Therefore

$$C_n A > C_n C_q > C_t > B. \quad \square$$

EXERCISES

1   Prove Theorem 85.

2   Complete the proof of Theorem 87.

3   Complete [3] in the proof of Theorem 88.

4   Prove Theorem 95.

5   If $A \in \mathbf{K}$ and $A = C_q$ for some $q \in \mathbf{Q}$, then we shall call A a *rational real number*. If $A \in \mathbf{K}$ and $A \neq C_q$ for every $q \in \mathbf{Q}$, then we shall call A an *irrational real number*. Prove that between any two rational real numbers C_a and C_b there is an irrational real number. [Hint: Try $C_a + (C_b - C_a)B^{-1}$, where B is the cut of Theorem 66.]

6   Prove that between any two distinct real numbers there is an irrational real number (see Exercise 5).

The Complete Ordered Field

So far, we have produced no property of the real number field that is not also a property of the rational number field. It would be a pity to have gone to all the trouble of manufacturing real numbers if they didn't turn out to be "better" in some sense or other than the rational numbers.

98   DEFINITION

Let $(F; +, \cdot; F_p)$ be an ordered field, let S be a subset of F, and let b be an element of F. We shall say that b is an *upper bound* of S iff $x \leq b$ for every $x \in S$. We shall say that b is a *least upper bound* of S, and write "$b = \text{lub } S$," iff b is an upper bound of S but no element of F smaller than b is an upper bound of S.

As a matter of fact, if a set in an ordered field has a least upper bound at all, it has exactly one; the proof is to be done as an exercise.

99   THEOREM

A set in an ordered field has at most one least upper bound.

We may, therefore, speak of *the* least upper bound of a set.

100   DEFINITION

An ordered field $(F; +, \cdot\ ; F_p)$ is said to be *complete* iff each nonempty subset of F that is bounded above has a least upper bound.

Here, at long last, is the property of the real number field that makes it a suitable place in which to do analysis:

101   THEOREM   Hauptsatz

The ordered field $(\mathbf{K}; +, \cdot\ ; \mathbf{K}_p)$ is complete.

Proof

Let $\mathscr{S}$ be a nonempty subset of $\mathbf{K}$ that is bounded above. Let B be an upper bound of $\mathscr{S}$, and let

$$L = \{x \in \mathbf{Q} : x \in A \text{ for some } A \in \mathscr{S}\}\ (= \cup\{A : A \in \mathscr{S}\}).$$

We shall show that $L \in \mathbf{K}$.

[1] Since $\mathscr{S}$ is nonempty there exists a cut A such that $A \in \mathscr{S}$. Since A is a cut, there exists a rational number q such that $q \in A$. Then $q \in L$, and so $L \neq \varnothing$.

The upper bound B of $\mathscr{S}$ is a cut, and so there is a rational number r such that $r \notin B$. Then $C_r \geq B$ ($x \in B$ implies $x < r$), so $C_r \geq A$ for every $A \in \mathscr{S}$. Therefore $A \subset C_r$ for every $A \in \mathscr{S}$. Since $r \notin C_r$, it follows that $r \notin A$ for every $A \in \mathscr{S}$. Therefore $r \notin L$, and so $L \neq \mathbf{Q}$.

[2] Assume that $a \in L$ and $b < a$. Then there exists $A \in \mathscr{S}$ such that $a \in A$. Since A is a cut and $b < a$, $b \in A$. Therefore $b \in L$.

[3] Assume that $a \in L$. Then there exists $A \in \mathscr{S}$ such that $a \in A$. Since A is a cut, there exists a rational number $b \in A$ such that $b > a$. But $b \in A$ implies $b \in L$. Therefore L is a cut.

We next show that L is an upper bound of $\mathscr{S}$. Assume $A \in \mathscr{S}$. If

$x \in A$, then $x \in L$ by definition of L. Hence $A \subset L$, and so $A \leq L$. Therefore L is an upper bound of S.

Finally, let T be any real number (cut) that is an upper bound of $\mathscr{S}$. Then $A \leq T$ for every $A \in \mathscr{S}$. Suppose $x \in L$. Then $x \in A$ for some $A \in \mathscr{S}$. Since $A \leq T$, $A \subset T$, and so $x \in T$. Therefore $L \subset T$, and so $L \leq T$. Therefore L is the least upper bound of $\mathscr{S}$. $\square$

In view of Theorem 95, we shall no longer be fussy about the distinction between a rational number q and the corresponding rational real number C_q. In fact, we shall henceforth consider **N**, **Z**, and **Q** to be subsets of **K**, and we shall denote members of **K** by lower-case letters, and subsets of **K** by capital letters.

Although we shall not attempt to prove it here, there is essentially only one complete ordered field. That is, if $(F; +, \cdot ; F_p)$ is a complete ordered field, then there exists a one-to-one order-preserving mapping of F onto **K** that also preserves sums and products.†

EXERCISES

1   Show by means of an example that the ordered field of rational numbers is not complete. [Hint: Look at the cut B of Theorem 66.]

2   Formulate definitions for *lower bound* and *greatest lower bound* of a set.

3 ▷ Prove that in a complete ordered field every nonempty subset that is bounded below has a greatest lower bound. [Hint: glb $S = -\text{lub}\{-x : x \in S\}$]

4   Let a **K**-*cut* be a nonempty proper subset of **K** having no largest member and containing all real numbers less than each of its members. Prove that there is a one-to-one mapping of the set of all **K**-cuts onto **K**, so that we obtain nothing essentially new by cutting **K**.

5 ▷ Let S be a nonempty set of real numbers and let $l \in$ **K**. Prove that if $s \leq l$ for every $s \in S$, and if for every $\varepsilon > 0$ there exists $s_\varepsilon \in S$ such that

$$s_\varepsilon > l - \varepsilon,$$

then l is the least upper bound of S.

6 ▷ State and prove the greatest lower bound analog of Exercise 5.

† For a proof of this fact, the reader is referred to Donald J. Lewis, *Introduction to Algebra* (New York: Harper & Row, 1965).

Denumerable Sets

Although the reader probably has a pretty good idea of what an infinite set is, there are some rather subtle notions relating to infinite sets that require more than just a pretty good idea for their mastery. These notions are particularly interesting and relevant when applied to certain subsets of **K**, and so we shall devote some attention to their development at this point.

102 DEFINITION

A set S is said to be *finite* iff either S is empty or for some $n \in \mathbf{N}$ there exists a one-to-one mapping of S onto $\{1, \ldots, n\}$. A set S is said *infinite* iff it is not finite.

Thus, for example, the sets $\{1, 2, \ldots, 10\}$, $\{a, b, c\}$, and $\{\pi, \sqrt{2}, -1, 4\}$ are finite, while the sets **N** and **K** are evidently infinite.

103 DEFINITION

A set S is said to be *denumerable* iff there exists a one-to-one mapping of S onto **N**.

It is easy to see that **N** itself is denumerable. If N_1 is the set of all natural numbers greater than 1, then N_1 is denumerable, because the mapping that sends n into $n - 1$ is a one-to-one mapping of N_1 onto **N**. Similarly, the set N_k of all natural numbers greater than k is a denumerable set, since the mapping that sends n into $n - k$ is a one-to-one mapping of N_k onto **N**.

104 THEOREM

Let S and T be sets such that there exists a one-to-one mapping of S onto T. If S is denumerable, then T is denumerable, and if T is denumerable, then S is denumerable.

Proof

[1] Assume T is denumerable. Then there is a one-to-one mapping g of T onto **N**.

Let

$$h(s) = g(f(s)), s \in S,$$

where f is the one-to-one mapping of S onto T. Then h is a one-to-one mapping of S onto $\mathbf{N}$, and so S is denumerable.

[2] Now assume S is denumerable. If ψ is defined by

$$\psi(t) = s \qquad \text{iff} \quad t = f(s), t \in T,$$

then ψ is a one-to-one mapping of T onto S, thus reducing the problem to the case previously considered. $\square$

If E is the set of all even natural numbers, then E is denumerable because the mapping that sends n into $\frac{1}{2}n$ is a one-to-one mapping of E onto $\mathbf{N}$. Then, according to Theorem 104, the set A of all positive integral multiples of 6 is denumerable, because the mapping that sends n into $\frac{1}{3}n$ is a one-to-one mapping of A onto E (one could, of course, just as easily map A directly onto $\mathbf{N}$).

105 LEMMA

If S is a denumerable set, then $S = \{s_n : n \in \mathbf{N}\}$ with $s_i \neq s_j$ if $i \neq j$.

If for some $n \in \mathbf{N}$ there is a one-to-one mapping of a set S onto $\{1, \ldots, n\}$, that is, if S is finite, then $S = \{s_1, \ldots, s_n\}$ with $s_i \neq s_j$ if $i \neq j$.

Proof

Assume S is denumerable. Then there exists a one-to-one mapping f of S onto $\mathbf{N}$. Therefore, for each $n \in \mathbf{N}$ there exists one and only one element $s_n \in S$ such that $f(s_n) = n$.

Clearly $\{s_n : n \in \mathbf{N}\} \subset S$. Conversely, if $s \in S$, then $f(s) = n$ for some $n \in \mathbf{N}$, whence $s = s_n$, since s_n is the unique element of S with $f(s_n) = n$. Therefore

$$\{s_n : n \in \mathbf{N}\} = S.$$

The proof of the second assertion is left as an exercise for the reader. $\square$

Denumerable subsets can be found in every infinite set.

106 THEOREM

Every infinite set contains a denumerable subset.

Proof

Let S be an infinite set. Since S is not empty, there exists an element S_6 $s_1 \in S$. Since S is infinite, the set $S_2 = S - \{s_1\}$ is not empty. Therefore S_2 contains an element s_2, and $s_2 \neq s_1$ (because $s_2 \in S_2$ but $s_1 \notin S_2$).

If we take as induction hypothesis the existence of distinct elements $s_1, \ldots, s_p$ of S, then the set

$$S_{p+1} = S - \{s_1, \ldots, s_p\}$$

is not empty (for otherwise S would be the finite set $\{s_1, \ldots, s_p\}$) and so contains an element s_{p+1}. Furthermore, $s_{p+1} \neq s_1, \ldots, s_p$, because s_{p+1} is in S_{p+1}, but $s_1, \ldots, s_p$ are not.

Let $T = \{s_n : n \in \mathbf{N}\}$. Then $T \subset S$, and, since the mapping f defined by

$$f(s_n) = n, n \in \mathbf{N},$$

is a one-to-one mapping of T onto $\mathbf{N}$, T is denumerable. □

The mapping that sends n into $2n$ is a one-to-one mapping of $\mathbf{N}$ onto a proper subset of itself, namely the set of all positive even integers. Notice also that Axiom 2 for the natural numbers guarantees the existence of another one-to-one mapping of $\mathbf{N}$ onto a proper subset of itself. Far from being a unique property of $\mathbf{N}$, the existence of such one-to-one mappings is characteristic of all infinite sets. This fact will be established in the following sequence of lemmas.

107 LEMMA

If S is a denumerable set, then for some proper subset T of S there exists a one-to-one mapping of S onto T.

Proof

Since S is denumerable, it follows from Lemma 105 that

$$S = \{s_n : n \in \mathbf{N}\}$$

with $s_i \neq s_j$ if $i \neq j$. Let

$$T = \{s_{n+1} : n \in \mathbf{N}\}.$$

Then $T \subset S$, and $T \neq S$ because $s_1 \in S$ but $s_1 \notin T$. Finally, if

$$g(s_n) = s_{n+1}, n \in \mathbf{N},$$

then g is a one-to-one mapping of S onto T. □

The conclusion of Lemma 108 is actually true if S is *any* infinite set.

108 LEMMA

If S is an infinite set, then for some proper subset T of S there exists a one-to-one mapping of S onto T.

Proof

Since S is infinite, there exists a denumerable subset D of S (Theorem 106). Since D is denumerable, for some proper subset E of D there exists a one-to-one mapping f of D onto E. Define g as follows:

$$g(x) = \begin{cases} x & \text{if } x \in S - D \\ f(x) & \text{if } x \in D. \end{cases}$$

If $T = (S - D) \cup E$, then T is a proper subset of S (any element of D that is not an element of E is an element of S that is not an element of T) and g is a one-to-one mapping of S onto T. □

The next lemma asserts that if $n \in \mathbf{N}$, then no proper subset of a set of n elements can itself have as many as n elements.

109 LEMMA

If there exists a one-to-one mapping of a set S onto $\{1, \ldots, n\}$, $n \in \mathbf{N}$, and if T is a proper subset of S, then no one-to-one mapping of T into $\{1, \ldots, n\}$ is onto $\{1, \ldots, n\}$.

Proof

Let M be the set of all those natural numbers n for which Lemma 109 is true.

If there exists a one-to-one mapping of S onto $\{1\}$, then $S = \{s_1\}$. Therefore, the only proper subset T of S is $T = \varnothing$. Hence the only mapping of T into $\{1\}$ is the empty mapping ($T \times \{1\} = \varnothing$, so the only subset of $T \times \{1\}$ is $\varnothing$). The empty mapping is not onto $\{1\}$, so $1 \in M$.

Assume $p \in M$, $p > 1$. If there exists a one-to-one mapping of some set S onto $\{1, \ldots, p, p + 1\}$, then it follows from Lemma 105 that

$$S = \{s_1, \ldots, s_p, s_{p+1}\}$$

with $s_i \neq s_j$ if $i \neq j$. Let T be any proper subset of S, and let f be any one-to-one mapping of T into $\{1, \ldots, p, p + 1\}$. If $f(t) \neq p + 1$ for every $t \in T$, then f is not onto $\{1, \ldots, p, p + 1\}$, and we are done. Otherwise,

$$p + 1 = f(t_0)$$

for exactly one $t_0 \in T$. Since $T \subset S$,

$$t_0 = s_q$$

for exactly one q, $1 \leq q \leq p + 1$. Let

$$T_q = \{t \in T : t \neq s_q\}$$

and

$$S_q = \{s_i \in S : i \neq q\}.$$

Since T is a proper subset of S, and s_q is in both T and S, T_q is a proper subset of S_q. Moreover, the mapping α defined by

$$\alpha(s_i) = \begin{cases} i & \text{if} \quad 1 \leq i < q \\ i - 1 & \text{if} \quad q < i \leq p + 1 \end{cases}$$

is a one-to-one mapping of S_q onto $\{1, \ldots, p\}$. If we define g by

$$g(t) = f(t), \qquad t \in T_q,$$

then g is a one-to-one mapping of T_q into $\{1, \ldots, p\}$. Since $p \in M$, g is not onto $\{1, \ldots, p\}$. Hence there exists $u \in \mathbf{N}$, $1 \leq u \leq p$, such that $g(t) \neq u$ for all $t \in T_q$. Hence $f(t) \neq u$ for all $t \in T_q$. Finally,

$$f(t_0) = p + 1 > p \geq u,$$

and so $f(t) \neq u$ for all $t \in T$. Therefore $(p + 1) \in M$, and so $M = \mathbf{N}$. $\square$

110 LEMMA

If S is a finite set and T is any proper subset of S, then no mapping of S onto T is one-to-one.

Proof

Assume that S is a finite set, and assume that T is a proper subset of S such that there exists a one-to-one mapping f of S onto T. Let h be the one-to-one mapping of T onto S defined by

$$h(t) = s \qquad \text{iff} \qquad t = f(s).$$

Since S is finite, for some positive integer n there is a one-to-one mapping g of S onto $\{1, \ldots, n\}$. If α is defined by

$$\alpha(t) = g(h(t)),$$

then α is a one-to-one mapping of T onto $\{1, \ldots, n\}$. But, according to Lemma 109, no one-to-one mapping of T into $\{1, \ldots, n\}$ can be onto $\{1, \ldots, n\}$. Hence there is no one-to-one mapping of S onto T. $\square$

111 THEOREM

A set S is infinite if and only if there exists a one-to-one mapping of S onto a proper subset of itself.

Proof

Lemma 108 and Lemma 110.

112 COROLLARY

Every subset of a finite set is finite.

Proof

Let F be a subset of a set S. Assume F is infinite. Then there exists a one-to-one mapping g of F onto a proper subset T of F. Define h by

$$h(s) = \begin{cases} s & \text{if} \quad s \in S - F \\ g(s) & \text{if} \quad s \in F. \end{cases}$$

Then h is a one-to-one mapping of S onto $(S - F) \cup T$, a proper subset of S. Hence S is infinite. Therefore, if S is finite, so is F. $\square$

We are now in a position to observe that $\mathbf{N}$ itself is infinite. In fact, all denumerable sets are infinite.

113 COROLLARY

Every denumerable set is infinite.

Proof

Lemma 107 and Theorem 111.

We now turn our attention to properties of denumerable sets.

114 LEMMA

Every infinite subset of $\mathbf{N}$ is denumerable.

Proof

Let S be an infinite subset of $\mathbf{N}$. Then S is not empty, and so S has a smallest element. Let s_1 be this smallest element of S.

Assume that $s_1, \ldots, s_p$ have been defined so that s_{i+1} is the smallest element of S that is greater than s_i, $i = 1, \ldots, p - 1$. The set S_p defined by

$$S_p = \{s \in S : s > s_p\}$$

is not empty, for otherwise S would be a subset of the finite set $\{1, \ldots, s_p\}$, and so S would itself be finite. Let s_{p+1} be the smallest element of S_p.

Clearly $\{s_n : n \in \mathbf{N}\} \subset S$, and $s_i \neq s_j$ if $i \neq j$. Also $\{s_n : n \in \mathbf{N}\}$ is infinite (Corollary 113). Therefore, for each $m \in \mathbf{N}$ there exists $n \in \mathbf{N}$ such that $s_n > m$, for otherwise $\{s_n : n \in \mathbf{N}\}$ would be a subset of the finite set $\{1, \ldots, m\}$. Hence, given $s \in S$ there exists $n \in \mathbf{N}$ such that $s_n > s$. Let n^* be the smallest positive integer such that $s_{n^*} > s$. Now $n^* \neq 1$, because s_1 is the smallest element of S, whereas s_{n^*} is not. Hence $n^* > 1$. Consider s_{n^*-1}. Now it cannot be that

$$s_{n^*-1} < s < s_{n^*},$$

because s_{n^*} is the smallest member of S greater than s_{n^*-1}. Hence $s \leq s_{n^*-1}$. But if $s < s_{n^*-1}$, then, since $n^* - 1 < n^*$, we have a contradiction of the choice of n^*. Therefore $s = s_{n^*-1}$. It then follows that

$$\{s_n : n \in \mathbf{N}\} = S. \quad \square$$

115 THEOREM

Every infinite subset of a denumerable set is denumerable.

Proof

Let D be a denumerable set, and let S be any infinite subset of D. Since D is denumerable, there is a one-to-one mapping f of D onto $\mathbf{N}$. Let

$$S_f = \{f(s) : s \in S\}.$$

If S_f were finite, then there would be a one-to-one mapping α of S_f onto $\{1, \ldots, n\}$ for some $n \in \mathbf{N}$. The mapping ψ defined by

$$\psi(s) = \alpha(f(s)), s \in S$$

would then be a one-to-one mapping of S onto $\{1, \ldots, n\}$, contradicting the hypothesis that S is infinite. Hence S_f is an infinite subset of $\mathbf{N}$. It follows from Lemma 114 that S_f is denumerable. Therefore, by Theorem 104, S is denumerable. $\quad \square$

116 THEOREM

S₅   If D is a denumerable set, if F is a finite set, and if $D \cap F = \varnothing$, then $D \cup F$ is denumerable.

Proof

Since F is finite, for some $n \in \mathbf{N}$ there is a one-to-one mapping f of F onto $\{1, \ldots, n\}$. Since D is denumerable, there is a one-to-one mapping g of D onto $\mathbf{N}$. Let

$$h(x) = \begin{cases} f(x) & \text{if } x \in F \\ n + g(x) & \text{if } x \in D. \end{cases}$$

Then h is a one-to-one mapping of $D \cup F$ onto **N**, and so $D \cup F$ is denumerable. ☐

117 THEOREM

If D_1 and D_2 are denumerable sets, and if $D_1 \cap D_2 = \varnothing$, then $D_1 \cup D_2$ is denumerable.

Proof

Since D_i is denumerable, there exists a one-to-one mapping f_i of D_i onto **N**, $i = 1, 2$. Let

$$g(x) = \begin{cases} 2f_1(x) & \text{if } x \in D_1 \\ 2f_2(x) - 1 & \text{if } x \in D_2. \end{cases}$$

Then g is a one-to-one mapping of $D_1 \cup D_2$ onto **N**, and so $D_1 \cup D_2$ is denumerable. ☐

Using Theorem 117 together with the principle of finite induction, it is easy to show that if $D_1, \ldots, D_n$ are denumerable sets with $D_i \cap D_j = \varnothing$ if $i \neq j$, then $\cup \{D_i : i = 1, \ldots, n\}$ is denumerable. As a matter of fact, a much stronger result holds.

118 THEOREM

If D_n is a denumerable set for each $n \in$ **N**, and if $D_i \cap D_j = \varnothing$ whenever $i \neq j$, then $\cup \{D_n : n \in$ **N**$\}$ is denumerable.

Proof

Since each set D_n is denumerable, for each $n \in$ **N** there exists a one-to-one mapping f_n of D_n onto **N**. Let g be defined by

$$g(x) = 2^n 3^{f_n(x)} \qquad \text{iff} \quad x \in D_n.$$

Then g is a one-to-one mapping of $\cup \{D_n : n \in$ **N**$\}$ onto a subset M of **N**. Now M contains the infinite set $\{2 \cdot 3^p : p \in$ **N**$\}$, and so M is itself infinite (Corollary 112). It follows from Theorem 115 that M is denumerable. Therefore, by Theorem 104, $\cup \{D_n : n \in$ **N**$\}$ is denumerable. ☐

We conclude this chapter with a rather remarkable theorem.

119 THEOREM

The set $\mathbf{Q}$ of all rational numbers is denumerable.

Proof

We shall use the notation $(m, n) = 1$ to denote that m and n are integers whose only common (integral) factors are 1 and -1 (i.e., m and n are *relatively prime*). Recall that a *prime* is a positive integer p greater than 1 whose only (integral) factors are $\pm p$ and ± 1. The reader will be asked to prove as an exercise that the set of all primes is infinite.

For each $n \in \mathbf{N}$, let

$$D_n = \left\{ \frac{m}{n} : m \in \mathbf{N} \text{ and } (m, n) = 1 \right\}.$$

Then D_n is infinite, since it contains the infinite set

$$\left\{ \frac{p}{n} : p \text{ is a prime} \right\}.$$

Therefore D_n is an infinite subset of the denumerable set

$$\left\{ \frac{m}{n} : m \in \mathbf{N} \right\},$$

and so D_n is itself denumerable for each $n \in \mathbf{N}$. Moreover, $D_i \cap D_j = \varnothing$ if $i \neq j$. Therefore $\cup\{D_n : n \in \mathbf{N}\}$ is denumerable. But $\cup\{D_n : n \in \mathbf{N}\}$ is the set $\mathbf{Q}^+$ of all positive rational numbers. Since the mapping f defined by

$$f(x) = -x, x \in \mathbf{Q}^+$$

is a one-to-one mapping of $\mathbf{Q}^+$ onto the set $\mathbf{Q}^-$ of all negative rational numbers, it follows that $\mathbf{Q}^-$ is also denumerable. Finally,

$$\mathbf{Q} = (\mathbf{Q}^- \cup \{0\}) \cup \mathbf{Q}^+,$$

and so, by Theorems 116 and 117, $\mathbf{Q}$ is denumerable. $\square$

The reader should not jump to the conclusion that *all* infinite sets are denumerable. As a matter of fact, $\mathbf{K}$ is *not* denumerable. The reader will be asked to prove this fact as an exercise in Chapter 2 (Exercise 15, p. 91).

EXERCISES

1   Complete the proof of Lemma 105.

2   Prove that if for every finite subset F of a set S there exists an element $s_F \in S$ such that $s_F \notin F$, then S is an infinite set.

3   Prove that if S is an infinite set and F is a finite subset of S, then there exists an element $s_F \in S$ such that $s_F \notin F$.

4   Prove that if F_1 and F_2 are finite sets with $F_1 \cap F_2 = \emptyset$, then $F_1 \cup F_2$ is finite.

5   ▷ A set S is said to be *countable* iff S is either finite or denumerable. Prove that if C_1 and C_2 are countable sets with $C_1 \cap C_2 = \emptyset$, then $C_1 \cup C_2$ is countable.

6   Prove that every subset of a countable set is a countable set.

7   Prove that if C_1 and C_2 are countable sets, then $C_1 \cup C_2$ is countable.

8   Prove that if $C_1, \ldots, C_n$ are countable sets, then

$$\cup\{C_i : i = 1, \ldots, n\}$$

is countable.

9   Prove that if C_n is a countable set for every $n \in \mathbf{N}$, and if $C_i \cap C_j = \phi$ whenever $i \neq j$, then $\cup \{C_n : n \in \mathbf{N})$ is a countable set.

10   Prove that if C_n is a countable set for every $n \in \mathbf{N}$, then

$$\cup\{C_n : n \in \mathbf{N}\}$$

is also countable.

11   Prove that if $\mathscr{C}$ is a countable set each of whose members is itself a countable set, then

$$\cup\{C : C \in \mathscr{C}\}$$

is countable.

TOPOLOGICAL
= PROPERTIES
OF THE REALS

The key concept of real analysis is that of limit. We shall base our study of the theory of limits on the notion of limit of a sequence.

Sequences

120 DEFINITION

S_{15} A *sequence* in a set M is a *mapping* of **N** into M. If s is a sequence in set M, we shall usually denote the unique member of M associated by s with the positive integer n by s_n rather than by $s(n)$. For each positive integer n, s_n will be called the nth *term* of the sequence s. A sequence in a set B will also be described as a *sequence of b's*, $b \in B$ (for example, a sequence of real numbers, a sequence of sets, a sequence of functions).

Certain subsets of **K** come up in conversation sufficiently often to warrant a special notation. Specifically, if a and b are real numbers with $a < b$, then

$$[a, b] = \{x \in \mathbf{K} : a \le x \le b\},$$

$$]a, b[= \{x \in \mathbf{K} : a < c < b\},$$

$$[a, b[= \{x \in \mathbf{K} : a \le x < b\},$$

$$]a, b] = \{x \in \mathbf{K} : a < x \le b\}.$$

The first of the above is called the *closed interval* from a to b, the second the *open interval* from a to b, while the last two can be called either *half-open* or *half-closed*, depending upon one's frame of mind at the time.

Our first theorem deals with a sequence of closed intervals. A bunch of closed intervals that are all nestled together must have at least one point in common.

121   THEOREM

If I is a sequence of closed intervals such that

$$I_{n+1} \subset I_n \quad \text{for every} \quad n \in \mathbf{N},$$

then there exists $x_0 \in \mathbf{K}$ such that

$$x_0 \in I_n \quad \text{for every} \quad n \in \mathbf{N}.$$

Proof

For each $n \in \mathbf{N}$, let

$$I_n = [a_n, b_n].$$

Since $I_1 \supset I_2 \supset \cdots \supset I_n$ for each $n \in \mathbf{N}$, it follows that

$$a_1 \le a_2 \le \cdots \le a_n < b_n \le \cdots \le b_2 \le b_1$$

for each $n \in \mathbf{N}$. Hence the set

$$\{a_n : n \in \mathbf{N}\}$$

is bounded above by b_1 and the set $\{b_n : n \in \mathbf{N}\}$ is bounded below by a_1.

Let

$$a = \text{lub}\{a_n : n \in \mathbf{N}\},$$

and let $b = \text{glb}\{b_n : n \in \mathbf{N}\}$.

Assume $b < a$. Then, since a is the least upper bound of the a_n's, there exists $n_0 \in \mathbf{N}$ such that $a_{n_0} > b$. But b is the greatest lower bound of the b_n's, so there exists $n_1 \in \mathbf{N}$ such that

$$b_{n_1} < a_{n_0}.$$

Now if $n_1 > n_0$, then $n_1 = n_0 + k$, and so

$$a_{n_0} \leq a_{n_0+1} \leq \cdots \leq a_{n_0+k} = a_{n_1} < b_{n_1},$$

a contradiction. If $n_1 < n_0$, then $n_0 = n_1 + l$, so

$$a_{n_0} < b_{n_0} = b_{n_1+l} \leq \cdots \leq b_{n_1+1} \leq b_{n_1},$$

a contradiction.

If $n_1 = n_0$, then

$$a_{n_0} < b_{n_0} = b_{n_1},$$

a contradiction. Therefore it must be the case that $a \leq b$.

Let $x_0 = \frac{1}{2}(a + b)$. Then $a \leq x_0 \leq b$.

Given $n \in \mathbf{N}$, consider $I_n = [a_n, b_n]$. Now $a_n \leq a$ and $b_n \leq b$. Hence $a_n \leq a \leq x_0 \leq b \leq b_n$, and so $x_0 \in I_n$. $\square$

We now turn our attention to sequences of real numbers.

122 DEFINITION

Let s be a sequence in $\mathbf{K}$, and let l be a real number. We shall say that l is a *limit* of s iff for every positive real number ε there exists $n_\varepsilon \in \mathbf{N}$ such that

$$|s_n - l| < \varepsilon \qquad \text{for every} \quad n \geq n_\varepsilon.$$

Our definition of limit simply says that l is a limit of s iff s can be made as close to l as we please for all n sufficiently large. Fortunately, sequences can have at most one such limit.

123 THEOREM

A sequence s in $\mathbf{K}$ can have at most one limit.

Proof

Assume that l_1 and l_2 are both limits of some sequence s in $\mathbf{K}$, and assume that $l_1 \neq l_2$. Let $\varepsilon = \frac{1}{2}|l_1 - l_2|$. Since $\varepsilon > 0$, there exists $n_1 \in \mathbf{N}$ such that $|s_n - l_1| < \varepsilon$ for all $n \geq n_1$, and there exists $n_2 \in \mathbf{N}$ such that

$$|s_n - l_2| < \varepsilon \qquad \text{for all} \qquad n \geq n_2.$$

Let $n_3 = \max\{n_1, n_2\}$.†

Then $n_3 \geq n_1$ and $n_3 \geq n_2$. Hence

$$2\varepsilon = |l_1 - l_2| = |(l_1 - s_{n_3}) + (s_{n_3} - l_2)|$$

$$2\varepsilon \leq |l_1 - s_{n_3}| + |s_{n_3} - l_2|$$

$$\leq |s_{n_3} - l_1| + |s_{n_3} - l_2|$$

$$< \varepsilon + \varepsilon = 2\varepsilon$$

and so $\varepsilon < \varepsilon$, a contradiction. Therefore it must be the case that $l_1 = l_2$.

124 DEFINITION

We shall say that a sequence s in $\mathbf{K}$ is a *convergent* sequence iff there exists $l \in K$ such that l is the limit of s. We shall write $\lim s_n = l$ to denote that s is convergent and l is the limit of s. A sequence s in $\mathbf{K}$ will be called *divergent* iff s is not convergent.

[1] As an example, suppose we wish to show that $\lim 1/n^2 = 0$. In order to do so, we must show that

$$\left| \frac{1}{n^2} - 0 \right| = \left| \frac{1}{n^2} \right|$$

can be made as small as we please for all n sufficiently large. This means that for every $\varepsilon > 0$ the *solution set* of the inequality

$$\left| \frac{1}{n^2} \right| < \varepsilon$$

must contain a set of the form

$$\{s_n \in \mathbf{N} : n \geq n_\varepsilon\}$$

(such a set is called a *tail* of $\mathbf{N}$). If for some $\varepsilon > 0$ the solution set of

$$\left| \frac{1}{n^2} \right| < \varepsilon$$

does *not* contain such a "tail" of $\mathbf{N}$, then the statement $\lim 1/n^2 = 0$ is false.

We observe that

$$\left| \frac{1}{n^2} \right| = \frac{1}{n^2} \qquad \text{for every} \quad n \in \mathbf{N},$$

† "max S" denotes the largest element of set S.

and that $n^2 \geq n$ for every $n \in \mathbf{N}$. Therefore

$$\left| \frac{1}{n^2} \right| \leq \frac{1}{n} \qquad \text{for every} \quad n \in \mathbf{N}.$$

Now $1/n < \varepsilon$ if and only if $n\varepsilon > 1$. Given $\varepsilon > 0$, then, since $1 > 0$, the Archimedean order of the reals guarantees the existence of $n_\varepsilon \in \mathbf{N}$ such that $n_\varepsilon \cdot \varepsilon > 1$. If $n \geq n_\varepsilon$, then

$$\frac{1}{n} \leq \frac{1}{n_\varepsilon} < \varepsilon,$$

so that $|1/n^2| < \varepsilon$ for all $n \geq n_\varepsilon$. Therefore $\lim 1/n^2 = 0$.

[2] For a second example, suppose we wish to show that $\lim 1/n \neq 1$. We note that

$$\left| \frac{1}{n} - 1 \right| = 1 - \frac{1}{n}.$$

But $1/n \leq \frac{1}{2}$ for every $n \geq 2$, so that $|1/n - 1| \geq 1 - \frac{1}{2}$ for every $n \geq 2$. Therefore, there is no $n_{1/4} \in \mathbf{N}$ such that $|1/n - 1| < \frac{1}{4}$ for every $n \geq n_{1/4}$. That is, the solution set of $|1/n - 1| < \frac{1}{4}$ does not contain a tail of $\mathbf{N}$. Therefore $\lim 1/n \neq 1$.

[3] As a final example, suppose we wish to show that

$$\lim \frac{1}{2^n} = 0.$$

We solve the inequality

$$\left| \frac{1}{2^n} \right| = \frac{1}{2^n} < \varepsilon.$$

Now $1/2^n < \varepsilon$ iff $-\log 2^n < \log \varepsilon$, where log is any logarithmic function with base greater than 1 (10, for instance). We then have

$$-\log 2^n < \log \varepsilon,$$

iff

$$-n \log 2 < \log \varepsilon,$$

iff

$$-n < \frac{\log \varepsilon}{\log 2},$$

iff

$$n > \frac{-\log \varepsilon}{\log 2},$$

iff

$$n > \frac{\log \varepsilon^{-1}}{\log 2}.$$

Taking n_ε any integer greater than or equal to $\log \varepsilon^{-1}/\log 2$ will then do the trick. Therefore $\lim(1/2^n) = 0$.

Sequences whose terms are eventually close together are treated next.

125 DEFINITION

A sequence s in $\mathbf{K}$ is said to be a *Cauchy sequence* iff for every positive real number ε there exists $n_\varepsilon \in \mathbf{N}$ such that $|s_m - s_n| < \varepsilon$ for all $n \geq n_\varepsilon$ and all $m \geq n_\varepsilon$.

It seems that we have run across Cauchy sequences before.

126 LEMMA

Every convergent sequence in $\mathbf{K}$ is a Cauchy sequence.

Proof

Let s be a convergent sequence in $\mathbf{K}$. Then there exists $l \in \mathbf{K}$ such that $\lim s_n = l$. Given $\varepsilon > 0$, choose n_ε so that

$$|s_n - l| < \tfrac{1}{2}\varepsilon \qquad \text{for every} \quad n \geq n_\varepsilon.$$

If $m \geq n_\varepsilon$ and $n \geq n_\varepsilon$, then

$$|s_m - s_n| = |(s_m - l) + (l - s_n)|$$
$$\leq |s_m - l| + |s_n - l|$$
$$< \tfrac{1}{2}\varepsilon + \tfrac{1}{2}\varepsilon = \varepsilon.$$

Therefore s is a Cauchy sequence. $\square$

The converse of Lemma 127 is also true. Its proof, however, is not quite so simple.

127 LEMMA

If s is a Cauchy sequence in $\mathbf{K}$, then s is convergent.

Proof

Let s be a Cauchy sequence in $\mathbf{K}$. Then there exists $n_1 \in \mathbf{N}$ such that

$$|s_m - s_n| < \tfrac{1}{2} \qquad \text{for all} \quad m \geq n_1 \text{ and all } n \geq n_1,$$

so

$$-\tfrac{1}{2} < s_m - s_{n_1} < \tfrac{1}{2} \qquad \text{for all} \quad m \geq n_1,$$

so

$$s_{n_1} - \tfrac{1}{2} < s_m < s_{n_1} + \tfrac{1}{2} \qquad \text{for all} \quad m \geq n_1.$$

Let $I_1 = [s_{n_1} - 1, s_{n_1} + 1]$. Then $s_m \in I_1$ for all $m \geq n_1$. Now there exists $n_2^* \in \mathbf{N}$ such that $|s_m - s_n| < \frac{1}{4}$ for all $m \geq n_2^*$ and all $n \geq n_2^*$. Let $n_2 = \max\{n_1 + 1, n_2^*\}$. Then $n_2 > n_1$. Also $n_2 \geq n_2^*$, so $|s_m - s_n| < \frac{1}{4}$ for all $m \geq n_2$ and all $n \geq n_2$. Specifically, $|s_m - s_{n_2}| < \frac{1}{4}$ for all $m \geq n_2$, so that, as above, $s_{n_2} - \frac{1}{4} < s_m < s_{n_2} + \frac{1}{4}$ for all $m \geq n_2$. Let $I_2 = [s_{n_2} - \frac{1}{2}, s_{n_2} + \frac{1}{2}]$. Then $s_m \in I_2$ for all $m \geq n_2$.

Assume $x \in I_2$. Then $|x - s_{n_2}| \leq \frac{1}{2}$ by definition of I_2. Hence

$$|x - s_{n_1}| = |(x - s_{n_2}) + (s_{n_2} - s_{n_1})|$$

$$\leq |x - s_{n_2}| + |s_{n_2} - s_{n_1}|$$

$$\leq \tfrac{1}{2} + |s_{n_2} - s_{n_1}|$$

$$< \tfrac{1}{2} + \tfrac{1}{2} \text{ (because } n_2 > n_1)$$

$$= 1.$$

Therefore $x \in I_1$. It follows that $I_2 \subset I_1$.

Now assume that positive integers $n_1, n_2, \ldots, n_k$ have been chosen so that

$$n_1 < n_2 < \cdots < n_k,$$

$$I_1 \supset I_2 \supset \cdots \supset I_k \quad \text{where} \quad I_j = [s_{n_j} - 1/2^{j-1}, \; s_{n_j} + 1/2^{j-1}]$$

$$(j = 1, \ldots, k),$$

$$|s_m - s_n| < 1/2^j \quad \text{for all} \quad m \geq n_j, n \geq n_j \, (j = 1, \ldots, k),$$

and $s_m \in I_j$ for all $m \geq n_j \, (j = 1, \ldots, k)$.

Then there exists $n_{k+1}^* \in \mathbf{N}$ such that

$$|s_m - s_n| < \frac{1}{2^{k+1}} \quad \text{for all} \quad m \geq n_{k+1}^*, n \geq n_{k+1}^*.$$

Let $n_{k+1} = \max\{n_k + 1, n_{k+1}^*\}$. Then $n_{k+1} > n_k$. Also $n_{k+1} \geq n_{k+1}^*$, so

$$|s_m - s_n| < \frac{1}{2^{k+1}} \quad \text{for all} \quad m \geq n_{k+1}, n \geq n_{k+1}.$$

In particular,

$$|s_m - s_{n_{k+1}}| < \frac{1}{2^{k+1}} \quad \text{for all} \quad m \geq n_{k+1},$$

so

$$s_{n_{k+1}} - \frac{1}{2^{k+1}} < s_m < s_{n_{k+1}} + \frac{1}{2^{k+1}} \quad \text{for all} \quad m \geq n_{k+1}.$$

Let

$$I_{k+1} = \left[s_{n_{k+1}} - \frac{1}{2^k}, s_{n_{k+1}} + \frac{1}{2^k} \right].$$

Then

$$s_m \in I_{k+1} \qquad \text{for all} \quad m \geq n_{k+1}.$$

Assume $x \in I_{k+1}$. Then $|x - s_{n_{k+1}}| \leq \dfrac{1}{2^k}$. Hence

$$|x - s_{n_k}| = |(x - s_{n_{k+1}}) + (s_{n_{k+1}} - s_{n_k})|$$

$$\leq |x - s_{n_{k+1}}| + |s_{n_{k+1}} - s_{n_k}|$$

$$\leq \frac{1}{2^k} + |s_{n_{k+1}} - s_{n_k}|$$

$$< \frac{1}{2^k} + \frac{1}{2^k} \qquad \text{(because } n_{k+1} > n_k)$$

$$= \frac{2}{2^k} = \frac{1}{2^{k-1}}.$$

Therefore $x \in I_k$. It follows that $I_{k+1} \subset I_k$.

By induction, we have a sequence I of closed intervals and a sequence n of positive integers such that for every $k \in \mathbf{N}$,

$$I_{k+1} \subset I_k,$$

$$n_{k+1} > n_k,$$

$$s_m \in I_k \qquad \text{for all} \quad m \geq n_k$$

$$|s_m - s_n| < \frac{1}{2^k} \qquad \text{for all} \quad m \geq n_k, n \geq n_k,$$

and

$$I_k = \left[s_{n_k} - \frac{1}{2^{k-1}}, s_{n_k} + \frac{1}{2^{k-1}} \right].$$

By Theorem 121, there exists a real number x_0 such that $x_0 \in I_k$ for every $k \in \mathbf{N}$. We shall show that $\lim s_n = x_0$.

Since, by a previous example, $\lim(1/2^n) = 0$, given $\varepsilon > 0$ there exists $m_\varepsilon \in \mathbf{N}$ such that

$$\frac{1}{2^n} < \varepsilon \qquad \text{for all} \quad n \geq m_\varepsilon.$$

Let $k(\varepsilon) = m_\varepsilon + 2$. Then $k(\varepsilon) - 2 = m_\varepsilon$, so

$$\frac{1}{2^{k(\varepsilon)-2}} < \varepsilon.$$

If $n \geq n_{k(\varepsilon)}$, then

$$|s_n - x_0| \leq |s_n - s_{n_{k(\varepsilon)}}| + |x_0 - s_{n_{k(\varepsilon)}}|$$

$$< \frac{1}{2^{k(\varepsilon)}} + |x_0 - s_{n_{k(\varepsilon)}}| \qquad \text{(because } n \geq n_{k(\varepsilon)}\text{)}$$

$$\leq \frac{1}{2^{k(\varepsilon)}} + \frac{1}{2^{k(\varepsilon)-1}} \qquad \text{(because } x_0 \in I_{k(\varepsilon)}\text{)}$$

$$= \frac{3}{2^{k(\varepsilon)}} < \frac{4}{2^{k(\varepsilon)}} = \frac{1}{2^{k(\varepsilon)-2}} < \varepsilon.$$

Therefore $\lim s_n = x_0$, and so s is convergent. $\quad\square$

128 THEOREM   Cauchy Convergence Criterion

A sequence s in $\mathbf{K}$ is convergent if and only if s is a Cauchy sequence.

Proof

Lemmas 126 and 127.

We conclude this section with a slightly sharper version of Theorem 121.

129 THEOREM   Nested Interval Theorem

If I is a sequence of closed intervals such that $I_n = [a_n, b_n]$ and $I_{n+1} \subset I_n$ for every $n \in \mathbf{N}$, and if $\lim (b_n - a_n) = 0$, then there is exactly one $x_0 \in \mathbf{K}$ such that $x_0 \in I_n$ for every $n \in \mathbf{N}$.

Proof

That there is at least one such point x_0 follows from Theorem 121. Assume that $x_0 \in I_n$ for all $n \in \mathbf{N}$ and that $y_0 \in I_n$ for all $n \in \mathbf{N}$. Let $l = |x_0 - y_0|$. Then $l \geq 0$, and, since x_0 and y_0 are both in I_n for every n,

$$b_n - a_n \geq l \qquad \text{for every} \quad n \in \mathbf{N}.$$

Hence (see Exercise 6, p. 82)

$$\lim(b_n - a_n) \geq l.$$

But $\lim (b_n - a_n) = 0$, so we have $0 \leq l \leq 0$, whence $l = 0$. Therefore $x_0 = y_0$. $\quad\square$

EXERCISES

In Exercises 1 through 5, either prove that the given sequence is convergent, or prove that it is divergent.

1   $s_n = \dfrac{n-1}{n}$.

2   $s_n = \cos \dfrac{n\pi}{2}$.

3   $s_n = n$.

4   $s_n = (-1)^n$.

5   $s_n = \dfrac{n + (-1)^n}{n}$.

6   ▷ Prove that if s is a convergent sequence, a and b are real numbers, and if n_1 is a positive integer such that $a \le s_n \le b$ for all $n \ge n_1$, then $a \le \lim s_n \le b$.

Limit Theorems for Sequences

Given a sequence s in **K**, we can use Definition 122 to determine if a given number l is its limit. The question is, how do we have any inkling as to what number l we ought to try? Similarly, the Cauchy convergence criterion can be used to show that a sequence is convergent, but gives us no clue as to what the limit of the sequence is. In this section we shall develop a few techniques for finding the limits of certain convergent sequences in a more or less routine way.

130 DEFINITION

A sequence s in **K** is said to be
   [1] *monotone-increasing* (or *nondecreasing*),
   [2] *monotone-decreasing* (or *nonincreasing*),
   [3] *bounded above*,
   [4] *bounded below*,
   [5] *bounded*,
iff, respectively,

[1] $s_n \leq s_{n+1}$ for every $n \in \mathbf{N}$,

[2] $s_n \geq s_{n+1}$ for every $n \in \mathbf{N}$,

[3] there exists $u \in \mathbf{K}$ such that $s_n \leq u$ for every $n \in \mathbf{N}$,

[4] there exists $l \in \mathbf{K}$ such that $s_n \geq l$ for every $n \in \mathbf{N}$,

[5] s is bounded above and below.

All sequences from here on will be sequences in $\mathbf{K}$.

131 THEOREM

If s is monotone-increasing and bounded above, then s is convergent, and

$$\lim s_n = \text{lub } \{s_n : n \in \mathbf{N}\}.$$

If s is monotone-decreasing and bounded below, then s is convergent, and

$$\lim s_n = \text{glb } \{s_n : n \in \mathbf{N}\}.$$

Proof

Assume that s is monotone-increasing and bounded above. Then the set

$$\{s_n : n \in \mathbf{N}\}$$

is nonempty (it contains, for example, s_1) and bounded above. Let

$$l = \text{lub } \{s_n : n \in \mathbf{N}\} ;$$

the existence of l is guaranteed by the Hauptsatz of Chapter 1.

Given $\varepsilon > 0$, we have $l - \varepsilon < l$, and so there exists $n_\varepsilon \in \mathbf{N}$ such that

$$l - \varepsilon < s_{n_\varepsilon} \leq l$$

(because $l - \varepsilon$ is not an upper bound of $\{s_n : n \in \mathbf{N}\}$). But s is monotone-increasing, so if $n \geq n_\varepsilon$ then

$$l - \varepsilon < s_{n_\varepsilon} \leq s_n \leq l,$$

so

$$|s_n - l| = l - s_n < l - (l - \varepsilon) = \varepsilon.$$

Hence

$$\lim s_n = l.$$

A similar proof can be given for the monotone-decreasing-bounded-below case. The details are left as an exercise. $\square$

If a sequence is convergent, its terms can't get too large.

132 THEOREM

If s is a convergent sequence, then s is bounded.

Proof

Since s is convergent, s has a limit, say $\lim s_n = l$. Hence there exists $n_1 \in \mathbf{N}$ such that

$$|s_n - l| < 1 \qquad \text{for all} \quad n \geq n_1.$$

Then for all $n \geq n_1$,

$$-1 < s_n - l < 1,$$

so

$$l - 1 < s_n < l + 1.$$

Let

$$a = \min \{s_1, s_2, \ldots, s_{n_1 - 1}, l - 1\},$$
$$b = \max \{s_1, s_2, \ldots, s_{n_1 - 1}, l + 1\}.$$

Then $a \leq s_n \leq b$ for every $n \in \mathbf{N}$. Therefore s is bounded. □

Once a sequence heads toward zero, it isn't easy to keep it away.

133 THEOREM

If s is a bounded sequence and $\lim t_n = 0$, then $\lim s_n t_n = 0$.

Proof

Since s is bounded, there exists $b > 0$ such that $|s_n| \leq b$ for every $n \in \mathbf{N}$ (see Exercise 10, p. 89). Since $\lim t_n = 0$, given $\varepsilon > 0$ there exists $n_\varepsilon \in \mathbf{N}$ such that

$$|t_n| < \frac{\varepsilon}{b} \qquad \text{for all} \quad n \geq n_\varepsilon.$$

If $n \geq n_\varepsilon$, then

$$|s_n t_n| = |s_n| |t_n| < b \frac{\varepsilon}{b} = \varepsilon.$$

Therefore $\lim s_n t_n = 0$. □

The next theorem provides the machinery for breaking big problems up into little problems.

134 THEOREM

Let s and t be sequences such that $\lim s_n = l_1$ and $\lim t_n = l_2$. Then

[1] $\lim (s_n + t_n) = l_1 + l_2$;

[2] $\lim cs_n = cl_1$ for every $c \in \mathbf{K}$;

[3] $\lim s_n t_n = l_1 l_2$;

and

[4] $\lim \dfrac{s_n}{t_n} = \dfrac{l_1}{l_2}$, provided that $l_2 \neq 0$.

Proof

[1] Given $\varepsilon > 0$, choose n_1 so that $|s_n - l_1| < \frac{1}{2}\varepsilon$ for all $n \geq n_1$, and choose n_2 so that $|t_n - l_2| < \frac{1}{2}\varepsilon$ for all $n \geq n_2$.

Let $n_\varepsilon = \max \{n_1, n_2\}$. If $n \geq n_\varepsilon$, then

$$|(s_n + t_n) - (l_1 + l_2)| = |(s_n - l_1) + (t_n - l_2)|$$
$$\leq |s_n - l_1| + |t_n - l_2|$$
$$< \tfrac{1}{2}\varepsilon + \tfrac{1}{2}\varepsilon = \varepsilon.$$

Therefore $\lim (s_n + t_n) = l_1 + l_2$.

[2] If $c = 0$, then $cs_n = 0$ for every $n \in \mathbf{N}$, and so

$$|cs_n| = 0 < \varepsilon$$

for every $\varepsilon > 0$ and for all $n \geq 1$. Therefore

$$\lim cs_n = 0 = 0 \cdot l_1 = cl_1.$$

Now assume that $c \neq 0$. Given $\varepsilon > 0$, choose n_ε so that

$$|s_n - l_1| < \frac{\varepsilon}{|c|} \qquad \text{for all} \quad n \geq n_\varepsilon.$$

If $n \geq n_\varepsilon$, then

$$|cs_n - cl_1| = |c(s_n - l_1)|$$
$$= |c||s_n - l_1|$$
$$< |c|\frac{\varepsilon}{|c|} = \varepsilon.$$

Therefore $\lim cs_n = cl_1$.

[3] Since s is convergent, s is bounded (Theorem 132). Hence there exists a positive real number b such that $|s_n| \leq b$ for all $n \in \mathbf{N}$.

Assume $l_2 = 0$. It then follows from Theorem 133 that

$$\lim s_n t_n = 0 = l_1 \cdot 0 = l_1 \cdot l_2.$$

Assume $l_2 \neq 0$. Given $\varepsilon > 0$, choose n_1 so that

$$|s_n - l_1| < \frac{\varepsilon}{2|l_2|} \qquad \text{for all} \quad n \geq n_1,$$

and choose n_2 so that

$$|t_n - l_2| < \frac{\varepsilon}{2b} \qquad \text{for all} \quad n \geq n_2.$$

Let $n_\varepsilon = \max\{n_1, n_2\}$. If $n \geq n_\varepsilon$, then

$$
\begin{aligned}
|s_n t_n - l_1 l_2| &= |s_n t_n - s_n l_2 + s_n l_2 - l_1 l_2| \\
&\leq |s_n||t_n - l_2| + |l_2||s_n - l_1| \\
&< b\frac{\varepsilon}{2b} + |l_2|\frac{\varepsilon}{2|l_2|} = \tfrac{1}{2}\varepsilon + \tfrac{1}{2}\varepsilon = \varepsilon.
\end{aligned}
$$

Therefore $\lim s_n t_n = l_1 l_2$.

[4] In view of part [3], it suffices to show that if $\lim t_n = l_2 \neq 0$, then

$$\lim \frac{1}{t_n} = \frac{1}{l_2}.$$

If $l_2 > 0$, then there is a real number b such that $0 < b < l_2$. Then $l_2 - b > 0$, so there exists $n_1 \in \mathbf{N}$ such that for all $n \geq n_1$

$$|t_n - l_2| < l_2 - b,$$

so

$$b - l_2 < t_n - l_2 < l_2 - b,$$

whence

$$b < t_n < 2l_2 - b.$$

Since $b > 0$, it follows that

$$|t_n| > b > 0 \qquad \text{for all} \quad n \geq n_1.$$

If $l_2 < 0$, then there is a positive real number b such that

$$l_2 < -b < 0.$$

Since $-b - l_2 > 0$, there exists $n_1 \in \mathbf{N}$ such that for all $n \geq n_1$.

$$|t_n - l_2| < -b - l_2,$$

so

$$b + l_2 < t_n - l_2 < -b - l_2,$$

whence

$$b + 2l_2 < t_n < -b.$$

Hence

$$|t_n| > b > 0 \qquad \text{for all} \quad n \geq n_1.$$

Thus, in either case ($l_2 > 0$ or $l_2 < 0$), there exist $b > 0$ and $n_1 \in \mathbf{N}$ such that $|t_n| > b$ for all $n \geq n_1$.

Given $\varepsilon > 0$, choose $n_2 \in \mathbf{N}$ so that $|t_n - l_2| < \varepsilon|l_2|b$ for all $n \geq n_2$. Let $n_\varepsilon = \max\{n_1, n_2\}$. If $n \geq n_\varepsilon$, then

$$\left| \frac{1}{t_n} - \frac{1}{l_2} \right| = \left| \frac{l_2 - t_n}{t_n l_2} \right| = \frac{|t_n - l_2|}{|t_n| \, |l_2|}$$

$$< \frac{|t_n - l_2|}{b|l_2|} < \frac{\varepsilon|l_2|b}{b|l_2|} = \varepsilon.$$

Therefore

$$\lim \frac{1}{t_n} = \frac{1}{l_2}. \quad \square$$

We next provide solutions for some of the little problems.

135 THEOREM

[1] If there exist $c \in \mathbf{K}$ and $n_1 \in \mathbf{N}$ such that $s_n = c$ for all $n \geq n_1$, then $\lim s_n = c$.

[2] $\lim \dfrac{1}{n} = 0$.

[3] $\lim r^n = 0$ if $|r| < 1$.

Proof

[1] We have $|s_n - c| = |c - c| = 0 < \varepsilon$ for all $n \geq n_1$ and for every $\varepsilon > 0$.

[2] Given $\varepsilon > 0$, there exists (Archimedean order of $\mathbf{K}$) $n_\varepsilon \in \mathbf{N}$ such that $n_\varepsilon \varepsilon > 1$.

If $n \geq n_\varepsilon$, then

$$\left| \frac{1}{n} \right| = \frac{1}{n} \leq \frac{1}{n_\varepsilon} < \varepsilon.$$

Therefore $\lim 1/n = 0$.

[3] If $r = 0$, the assertion follows from part [1]. Assume, then, that

$r \neq 0$. Since $0 < |r| < 1$, we have $\log_{10} |r| < 0$. Given $\varepsilon > 0$, let $\varepsilon^* = \min \{\varepsilon, \frac{1}{2}\}$. Then $\varepsilon^* \leq \varepsilon$ and $\varepsilon^* \leq \frac{1}{2}$ so that $\log_{10} \varepsilon^* < 0$. Therefore

$$\frac{\log_{10} \varepsilon^*}{\log_{10} |r|} > 0,$$

and so (Archimedean order of **K**) there exists $n_\varepsilon \in \mathbf{N}$ such that

$$n_\varepsilon > \frac{\log_{10} \varepsilon^*}{\log_{10} |r|}.$$

If $n \geq n_\varepsilon$, then

$$n > \frac{\log_{10} \varepsilon^*}{\log_{10} |r|},$$

$$n \log_{10} |r| < \log_{10} \varepsilon^*,$$

$$\log_{10} |r|^n < \log_{10} \varepsilon^*,$$

$$|r|^n < \varepsilon^* \leq \varepsilon.$$

Hence $|r^n| < \varepsilon$ for all $n \geq n_\varepsilon$. Therefore $\lim r^n = 0$. $\square$

As an example of the application of these theorems, consider the problem of finding $\lim s_n$ if $s_n = (2n + 1)(3n - 2)/(n + 1)(n - 1)$.

$$s_n = \frac{(2n + 1)(3n - 2)}{(n + 1)(n - 1)} = \frac{6n^2 - n - 2}{n^2 - 1}$$

$$= \frac{6 - (1/n) - (2/n^2)}{1 - (1/n^2)}.$$

$$\lim s_n = \lim \frac{6 - (1/n) - (2/n^2)}{1 - (1/n^2)} = \frac{\lim[6 - (1/n) - (2/n^2)]}{\lim[1 - (1/n^2)]}$$

$$= \frac{\lim 6 + \lim[(-1)/n] + \lim(-2/n^2)}{\lim 1 + \lim((-1)/n^2)}$$

$$= \frac{6 + (-1)\lim(1/n) + (-2)\lim(1/n^2)}{1 + (-1)\lim(1/n^2)}$$

$$= \frac{6 + (-1)(0) - 2\lim(1/n)\lim(1/n)}{1 + (-1)\lim(1/n)\lim(1/n)}$$

$$= \frac{6 - (0) - (2)(0)(0)}{1 + (-1)(0)(0)} = 6.$$

EXERCISES

1 ▷ Prove that if $\lim s_n = l_1$ and $\lim t_n = l_2$, then

$$\lim (s_n - t_n) = l_1 - l_2.$$

2 ▷ Prove that for each (fixed) $k \in \mathbf{N}$,

$$\lim_n \frac{1}{n^k} = 0.$$

In Exercises 3 through 9, find $\lim s_n$—if it exists.

3   $s_n = \dfrac{(2n - 1)(n + 2)}{3n^2 + 5}.$

4   $s_n = \dfrac{n}{2n + 3} - 4^{-n}.$

5   $s_n = \dfrac{2n}{n^2 + 1}.$

6   $s_n = \dfrac{(-1)^n}{n}.$

7   $s_n = \dfrac{\cos(n\pi/2)}{n}.$

8   $s_n = 1 + r + r^2 + \cdots + r^{n-1}, |r| < 1.$

9   $s_n = \dfrac{n^3 - 1}{n}.$

10 ▷ Prove that if s is a bounded sequence, then there exists a positive real number b such that $|s_n| \le b$ for every $n \in \mathbf{N}$.

11 ▷ Prove that a monotone-increasing sequence is convergent if and only if it is bounded above.

12 Finish the proof of Theorem 131.

13 Give an example of sequences s and t such that $\lim(s_n + t_n)$ exists, but neither $\lim s_n$ nor $\lim t_n$ exists.

14 Definition. An ordered pair (q, s) with q a nonnegative integer and s a sequence in the set $\{0, 1, \ldots, 9\}$ is said to be a *decimal representation* of the positive real number (cut) A iff

    [1] $q \in A$ but $(q + 1) \notin A$, and

[2] for each positive integer n, the rational number

$$q + \frac{s_1}{10} + \frac{s_2}{10^2} + \cdots + \frac{s_n}{10^n}$$

is in A, but the rational number

$$q + \frac{s_1}{10} + \frac{s_2}{10^2} + \cdots + \frac{s_n}{10^n} + \frac{1}{10^n}$$

is not in A.

(a) Prove that $(1, s)$, where $s_n = 9$ for every $n \in \mathbf{N}$ is a decimal representation of C_2.

(b) Find a decimal representation of $C_{1/3}$.

(c) Prove that every positive real number (cut) has a decimal representation. [Hint: Construct a decimal representation of an arbitrary positive cut A by giving instructions as to how to choose q ; s_1 ; and s_{n+1} given $s_1, \ldots, s_n$. You will need to use the fact that $\mathbf{N}$ is well-ordered in order to show that your instructions can always be carried out, and do, in fact, yield a decimal representation of A.]

(d) Prove that every positive real number has at most one decimal representation (so that, in view of part (c), we may speak of *the* decimal representation of a real number). [Hint: Assume that (q, s) and $(q^\bullet, s^\bullet)$ are both decimal representations of the same positive cut A. Prove that $q = q^\bullet$ by showing that $q < q^\bullet$ and $q > q^\bullet$ are impossible. Similarly, prove that $s_1 = s_1^\bullet$, $s_2 = s_2^\bullet$, and so on.]

(e) Prove that if q is nonnegative integer and s is a sequence in the set $\{0, 1, \ldots, 9\}$ such that for each $n \in \mathbf{N}$ there exists $m \in \mathbf{N}$ such that $m > n$ and $s_m > 0$, then there exists a positive real number A such that (q, s) is the decimal representation of A. [Hint: Let

$$A = \left\{ x \in \mathbf{Q} : x < q + \frac{s_1}{10} + \cdots + \frac{s_n}{10^n} \quad \text{for some} \quad n \in \mathbf{N} \right\}.$$

Prove that A is a positive cut and that (q, s) is the decimal representation of A.]

(f) Prove that distinct positive real numbers have distinct decimal representations. [Hint: Let A and B be distinct positive real numbers with decimal representations (q, s) and (r, t), respectively. There is no loss of generality in assuming that $A < B$. Then there is a rational number b_0 such that $b_0 \in B$ but

$b_0 \notin A$. Since B is a cut, there exists $b_1 \in B$ such that $b_1 > b_0$. Choose $n_0 \in \mathbf{N}$ so that $10^{-n_0} < b_1 - b_0$. Now show that

$$q + \frac{s_1}{10} + \cdots + \frac{s_{n_0}}{10^{n_0}} < r + \frac{t_1}{10} + \cdots + \frac{t_{n_0}}{10^{n_0}}.$$

If $q \geq r$, $s_1 \geq t_1, \ldots$, and $s_{n_0} \geq t_{n_0}$, then the above inequality is contradicted. Hence at least one of $q < r$, $s_1 < t_1, \ldots$, or $s_{n_0} < t_{n_0}$ is true.]

15 Prove that the set $\mathbf{K}$ is not denumerable. [Hint: Use decimal representations to prove that $[0, 1]$ is not a denumerable set.]

Open and Closed Sets

Introducing some of the language of point-set topology will give us a means of describing in deceptively simple language some rather profound concepts.

136 DEFINITION

Let x be a real number. A set $I \subset \mathbf{K}$ is said to be a *neighborhood* of x iff I is an open interval such that $x \in I$.

Let S be a subset of $\mathbf{K}$. A real number x is said to be an *interior point* of S iff there exists a neighborhood I of x such that $I \subset S$. The *interior* of S, denoted by "Int S," is the set

$$\{x \in \mathbf{K} : x \text{ is an interior point of } S\}.$$

Let S be a subset of $\mathbf{K}$. The set S is said to be *open* iff $S \subset \text{Int } S$. The set S is said to be *closed* iff $C_{\mathbf{K}}(S)$ is open.

S_6

By way of example, every open interval $]a, b[$ is a neighborhood of each of its points; therefore every such interval contains a neighborhood of each of its points; and therefore every such interval is an open set. The closed interval $[0, 1]$ is not an open set because, for example, no neighborhood of 0 is contained in the set; the complement of $[0, 1]$

is open, however, and so [0, 1] itself is closed. Every set of the form [*a*, *b*[is neither open nor closed, since the set contains no neighborhood of *a* while its complement contains no neighborhood of *b*.

137 DEFINITION

Let *x* be a real number and let *S* be a subset of **K**. Then *x* is said to be a *cluster point* (or *limit point*, or *point of accumulation*) of *S* iff for every neighborhood *I* of *x* there exists $y \in S$ with $y \neq x$ such that $y \in I$ (i.e. every neighborhood of *x* contains a point of *S* different from *x*). The *derivative* of *S*, denoted by *D*(*S*) is the set

$$\{x \in \mathbf{K} : x \text{ is a cluster point of } S\}.$$

Again by way of example, the derivative of [*a*, *b*],]*a*, *b*[, [*a*, *b*[, and]*a*, *b*] is [*a*, *b*]. The derivative of **N** is the empty set, and the derivative of **Q** is **K**.

EXERCISES

In Exercises 1 through 8, find the interior and the derivative of the given set. Then determine if the given set is open, closed, both, or neither.

1   [−1, 1]

2   ]−1, 1]

3    $[-\sqrt{2}, \pi]$

4   **Z**

5   **Q**

6    $\left\{\dfrac{1}{n} : n \in \mathbf{N}\right\}$

7   {0}

8   **K**

9   ▷ Let *S* be a subset of **K**. Prove that *S* is open if and only if *S* contains a neighborhood of each of its points.

10   Prove that the union of any collection of open subsets of **K** is an open set.

11   Prove that the intersection of any collection of closed subsets of **K** is a closed set.

12   Prove that given any subset *S* of **K** there exists one and only one set S^- such that
(a) S^- is closed,
(b) $S^- \supset S$, and
(c) if *F* is any closed set containing *S*, then $F \supset S^-$.
The set S^- is called the *closure* of *S*.

13   Find the closure of each of the sets in Exercises 1 through 8.

14   Prove that for every $S \subset \mathbf{K}$, $S^- = S \cup D(S)$.

Compact Sets

When we say that a set S is compact, we mean, stated somewhat informally, that no matter how ingenious we try to be about covering up S by pasting infinitely many open sets all over it, we could save a great deal of time and effort, because only a finite number of our ingeniously-placed open sets are actually needed to cover up S entirely. The following definitions formalize this notion.

138 DEFINITION

A collection $\mathscr{C}$ of sets is said to be a *covering* of a set S iff

S_7
$$S \subset \cup \{M : M \in \mathscr{C}\}.$$

A collection $\mathscr{C}_1$ is said to be a *subcovering* of $\mathscr{C}$ relative to S iff

$$\mathscr{C}_1 \subset \mathscr{C} \qquad \text{and} \qquad S \subset \cup \{M : M \in \mathscr{C}_1\}.$$

139 DEFINITION

A covering $\mathscr{C}$ of a set of real numbers is said to be an *open* covering of S iff each member of $\mathscr{C}$ is an open subset of $\mathbf{K}$.

Thus, for example, the collection $\{[1/n, 2[: n \in \mathbf{N}\}$ is a covering of $]0, 2]$, but it is not an open covering of $]0, 2[$.

140 DEFINITION

A set S of real numbers is said to be *compact* iff each open covering of S has a finite subcovering relative to S.

Not all subsets of $\mathbf{K}$ are compact. In particular, the biggest subset of $\mathbf{K}$ is not.

141 THEOREM

The set $\mathbf{K}$ is not compact.

Proof

For each $n \in \mathbf{N}$, let

$$G_n = \,]-n, n[.$$

Then $\{G_n : n \in \mathbf{N}\}$ is an open covering of $\mathbf{K}$. If $\{n_1, \ldots, n_k\}$ is any finite subset of $\mathbf{N}$, then

$$\cup\{G_n : n = n_1, \ldots, n_k\} = \,]-p, p[\,\neq \mathbf{K},$$

where $p = \max\{n_1, \ldots, n_k\}$. Hence $\{G_n : n \in \mathbf{N}\}$ has no finite sub-covering relative to $\mathbf{K}$, and so $\mathbf{K}$ is not compact. $\square$

On the other hand, compact sets *do* exist.

142 THEOREM

Every closed interval $[a, b]$ is compact.

Proof

Let $\mathscr{C}$ be any open covering of $[a, b]$. Let M be the set of all real numbers x in $]a, b]$ having the property that $\mathscr{C}$ has a finite subcovering relative to $[a, x]$.

The set M is not empty: Since $\mathscr{C}$ covers $[a, b]$, there is an open set $G_a \in \mathscr{C}$, such that $a \in G_a$. Since G_a is open, there exists an open interval $I = \,]p, q[,\ q \leq b$, such that

$$a \in \,]p, q[\,\subset G_a.$$

Then $p < a < q$, so

$$p < a < \tfrac{1}{2}(a + q) < q \leq b.$$

Hence

$$[a, \tfrac{1}{2}(a + q)] \subset \,]p, q[\,\subset G_a.$$

Therefore

$$\tfrac{1}{2}(a + q) \in M.$$

The set M is bounded above: If $x \in M$, then $x \in \,]a, b[$, and so $x \leq b$. Hence b is an upper bound of M.

Therefore M has a least upper bound u (Theorem 101) and $u \leq b$.

We shall assume that $u < b$ and show that this leads to a contradiction. Now $u \in [a, b]$, so there exists $G_u \in \mathscr{C}$ such that $u \in G_u$. Since G_u is open, there exists an open interval $]c, d[$ such that

$$c < u < d \leq b \qquad \text{and} \qquad]c, d[\,\subset G_u.$$

Now $c < u = \text{lub } M$, so there is an $m \in M$ such that $c < m < u$. Since $m \in M$, $\mathscr{C}$ has a finite subcovering relative to $[a, m]$. But

$$[a, d[\subset [a, m] \cup]c, d[\subset [a, m] \cup G_u$$

so $\mathscr{C}$ has a finite subcovering relative to $[a, d[$. Since $u < d$, we have

$$u < \tfrac{1}{2}(u + d) < d,$$

whence

$$[a, \tfrac{1}{2}(u + d)] \subset [a, d[.$$

Therefore $\mathscr{C}$ has a finite subcovering relative to $[a, \tfrac{1}{2}(u + d)]$, and so $\tfrac{1}{2}(u + d) \in M$. Therefore $\tfrac{1}{2}(u + d) \leq \text{lub } M = u$. But we also have $\tfrac{1}{2}(u + d) > u$. This contradiction implies that $u = b$.

Since $b \in [a, b]$ there is an open set $G_b \in \mathscr{C}$ such that $b \in G_b$. Since G_b is open, there exists an open interval $]p, q[$ such that

$$p < b < q \qquad \text{and} \qquad]p, q[\subset G_b.$$

Since $p < b = \text{lub } M$, there is a number $m \in M$ such that $p < m < b$. Then $\mathscr{C}$ has a finite subcovering relative to $[a, m]$. But

$$[a, b] \subset [a, m] \cup]p, q[\subset [a, m] \cup G_b.$$

Hence $\mathscr{C}$ has a finite subcovering relative to $[a, b]$. $\square$

A more general version of Theorem 142 is now relatively easy to establish.

143 THEOREM

If S is a bounded and closed subset of $\mathbf{K}$, then S is compact.

Proof

Since S is bounded, there is a closed interval $[a, b]$ such that $S \subset [a, b]$. Let $\mathscr{C}$ be any open covering of S. Then $\mathscr{C}^{\bullet} = \mathscr{C} \cup \{C_{\mathbf{K}}(S)\}$ is an open covering of $\mathbf{K}$ and hence of $[a, b]$. Since $[a, b]$ is compact, $\mathscr{C}^{\bullet}$ has a finite subcovering $\mathscr{D}^{\bullet}$ relative to $[a, b]$. Let

S_6

$$\mathscr{D} = \underline{\mathscr{D}^{\bullet} - \{C_{\mathbf{K}}(S)\}}.$$

Then D is a finite subcovering of $\mathscr{C}$ relative to $[a, b]$. $\square$

The condition that a set be bounded and closed is also a necessary condition for compactness.

144 LEMMA

If S is a compact subset of $\mathbf{K}$, then S is bounded.

Proof

The collection

$$\mathscr{C} = \{]x - 1, x + 1[\,:\, x \in S\}$$

is an open covering of S. Hence $\mathscr{C}$ has a finite subcovering relative to S, say $\{]x_i - 1, x_i + 1[\,:\, i = 1, \ldots, n\}$.

Let

$$a = \min\{x_1, \ldots, x_n\},$$

and let

$$b = \max\{x_1, \ldots, x_n\}.$$

If $s \in S$, then $s \in \,]x_i - 1, x_i + 1[$ for some i, $1 \le i \le n$. But then

$$a - 1 \le x_i - 1 < s < x_i + 1 \le b + 1.$$

Hence $a - 1 \le s \le b + 1$ for every $s \in S$. Therefore S is bounded. $\Box$

145 LEMMA

If S is a compact subset of $\mathbf{K}$ then S is closed.

Proof

We shall show that $C_{\mathbf{K}}(S)$ is open.

Assume that $x \in C_{\mathbf{K}}(S)$. Then for each $s \in S$ there are neighborhoods U_s of x and V_s of s such that

$$U_s \cap V_s = \varnothing$$

(for example, let $U_s = \,]x - \frac{1}{4}|x - s|, x + \frac{1}{4}|x - s|[$, $V_s = \,]s - \frac{1}{4}|x - s|,$ $s + \frac{1}{4}|x - s|[$). The collection $\{V_s : s \in S\}$ is then an open covering of S. Hence there is a finite subcovering relative to S, say

$$\{V_{s_i} : i = 1, \ldots, n\}.$$

Consider the collection

$$\{U_{s_i} : i = 1, \ldots, n\}.$$

Each U_{s_i} is a neighborhood of x and so is of the form $]a_i, b_i[$, $a_i < x < b_i$. Let

$$a = \max\{a_1, \ldots, a_n\},$$

$$b = \min\{b_1, \ldots, b_n\}.$$

Then $a_i \leq a < x < b \leq b_i$, $i = 1, \ldots, n$. Hence $]a, b[$ is a neighborhood of x and $]a, b[\subset U_{s_i}$ for every $i = 1, \ldots, n$.

Suppose that there exists $p \in \mathbf{K}$ such that

$$p \in]a, b[\cap (\cup\{V_{s_i} : i = 1, \ldots, n\}).$$

Then $p \in]a, b[$ and $p \in V_{s_i}$ for some i, $1 \leq i \leq n$. Since $]a, b[\subset U_{s_i}$, we have $p \in U_{s_i}$ and $p \in V_{s_i}$ for some i, a contradiction of

$$U_{s_i} \cap V_{s_i} = \varnothing \qquad \text{for every } i.$$

Therefore

$$]a, b[\cap (\cup\{V_{s_i} : i = 1, \ldots, n\}) = \varnothing.$$

since

$$\cup\{V_{s_i} : i = 1, \ldots, n\} \supset S,$$

$$]a, b[\cap S = \varnothing.$$

Therefore $]a, b[\subset C_{\mathbf{K}}(S)$. Since $]a, b[$ is a neighborhood of x, it follows that $C_{\mathbf{K}}(S)$ is open. Hence S is closed. $\square$

146 THEOREM   Heine–Borel Theorem

A subset S of $\mathbf{K}$ is compact if and only if S is bounded and closed.

Proof

Theorem 143, Lemma 144 and Lemma 145.

If infinitely many points are put in a compact set, then lots of them are very close together.

147 THEOREM

If S is compact and A is an infinite subset of S, then A has at least one cluster point in S.

Proof

Assume that A has no cluster points in S. Then for each $s \in S$ there is a neighborhood N_s of s that contains no point of A except (possibly) s itself. That is, N_s contains at most one point of A.

Now $\{N_s : s \in S\}$ is an open covering of S. Hence there is a finite subcovering relative to S, say

$$\{N_{s_i} : i = 1, \ldots n\}.$$

Then $\{N_{s_i} : i = 1, \ldots, n\}$ covers S, and hence covers A. Therefore A contains at most n points, a contradiction. Hence A has at least one cluster point in S. $\square$

Theorem 147 is often useful when stated in a slightly different way.

148 THEOREM   Bolzano–Weierstrass Theorem

Every bounded infinite subset A of **K** has at least one cluster point (in **K**).

Proof

Since A is bounded, there are real numbers p and q such that $p \leq a \leq q$ for every $a \in A$. Then $A \subset [p, q]$. But $[p, q]$ is compact, and so A has at least one cluster point in $[p, q]$, and hence in **K**.

EXERCISES

1   Prove that p is a cluster point of a set M if and only if there exists a sequence s in M such that

$$s_n \neq p \qquad \text{for every } n \in \mathbf{N}$$

and

$$\lim s_n = p.$$

2   Prove that if A is a bounded infinite subset of **K**, then there exists a sequence s in A such that s is a Cauchy sequence.

3   A sequence t is said to be a *subsequence* of a sequence s iff there exists a sequence p in **N** such that

$$p_n < p_{n+1} \qquad \text{for every } n \in \mathbf{N}$$

and

$$t_n = s_{p_n} \qquad \text{for every } n \in \mathbf{N}.$$

Prove that if s is a bounded sequence, then there exists a Cauchy sequence t such that t is a subsequence of s.

4   Give an example of a divergent sequence that has a convergent subsequence.

5   Prove that every open covering of **K** has a countable subcovering relative to **K**. [This is *not* an easy exercise.]

Limit of a Mapping

Following time-honored mathematical tradition, we shall write

$$\lim_{x \to a} f(x) = l$$

when and only when $f(x)$ is as close to l as we please for all x sufficiently close to (but different from) a. In order to be sure that there *are*, in fact, x's sufficiently close to a, we shall require that a be a cluster point of the *domain* of f.

S_{14}

149 DEFINITION

Let S be a set of real numbers, let f be a mapping of S into $\mathbf{K}$, and let $a \in \mathbf{K}$. We shall say that the real number l is a *limit of* $f(x)$ *as x tends to a* iff $a \in D(S)$ and iff for every $\varepsilon > 0$ there exists $\delta_\varepsilon > 0$ such that $|f(x) - l| < \varepsilon$ for all $x \in S$ with $0 < |x - a| < \delta_\varepsilon$. We shall say that $f(x)$ *has no limit as x tends to a* iff no such real number l exists.

It turns out, of course, that a mapping can have at most one limit as x tends to a, so that we can come right out and talk about *the* limit of $f(x)$ as x tends to a. The proof is left as an exercise.

150 THEOREM

If f is a mapping of S into $\mathbf{K}$ and $a \in D(S)$, then $f(x)$ has at most one limit as x tends to a.

151 DEFINITION

We shall write $\lim_{x \to a} f(x) = l$ iff l is the limit of $f(x)$ as x tends to a. We shall say that $\lim_{x \to a} f(x)$ *does not exist* iff $f(x)$ has no limit as x tends to a.

We can readily develop the theory of limits for mappings by using what we already know about limits of sequences together with the following theorem.

152 THEOREM

Let f be a mapping of S into $\mathbf{K}$, and let $a \in D(S)$. Then $\lim_{x \to a} f(x) = l$

if and only if $\lim f(s_n) = l$ for every sequence s in $C_S(\{a\})$ such that $\lim s_n = a$.

Proof

Assume that $\lim_{x \to a} f(x) = l$. Let s be any sequence in $C_s(\{a\})$ such that $\lim s_n = a$. We must show that $\lim f(s_n) = l$.

Given $\varepsilon > 0$ there exists $\delta_\varepsilon > 0$ such that $|f(x) - l| < \varepsilon$ for every $x \in S$ with $0 < |x - a| < \delta_\varepsilon$. Since $\lim s_n = a$ and $\delta_\varepsilon > 0$, there exists $n_\varepsilon \in \mathbf{N}$ such that

$$|s_n - a| < \delta_\varepsilon \qquad \text{for every} \quad n \geq n_\varepsilon.$$

Since s is a sequence in $C_S(\{a\})$, $s_n \neq a$ for every n, and so

$$0 < |s_n - a| < \delta_\varepsilon \qquad \text{for every} \quad n \geq n_\varepsilon.$$

Therefore

$$|f(s_n) - l| < \varepsilon \qquad \text{for every} \quad n \geq n_\varepsilon,$$

and so

$$\lim f(s_n) = l.$$

Conversely, assume that $\lim_{x \to a} f(x) \neq l$. Then there is a real number $\varepsilon_0 > 0$ with the property that for every $\delta > 0$ there exists an $x_\delta \in S$ such that $0 < |x_\delta - a| < \delta$ and $|f(x_\delta) - l| \geq \varepsilon_0$. Hence, for every $n \in \mathbf{N}$ there exists $s_n \in S$ such that $0 < |s_n - a| < 1/n$ and $|f(s_n) - l| \geq \varepsilon_0$ (take $s_n = x_{1/n}$).

Consider the sequence s defined above. Since $|s_n - a| > 0$ for every n, s is a sequence in $C_S(\{a\})$. Moreover, given $\varepsilon > 0$, choose $n_\varepsilon \in \mathbf{N}$ so large that

$$\frac{1}{n_\varepsilon} < \varepsilon.$$

If $n \geq n_\varepsilon$, then

$$|s_n - a| < \frac{1}{n} \leq \frac{1}{n_\varepsilon} < \varepsilon.$$

Hence $\lim s_n = a$. However $|f(s_n) - l| \geq \varepsilon_0$ for every $n \in \mathbf{N}$ and so $\lim f(s_n) \neq l$. Therefore, if $\lim_{x \to a} f(x) \neq l$, then there exists a sequence s in $C_S(\{a\})$ such that $\lim s_n = a$ but $\lim f(s_n) \neq l$. Hence if $\lim s_n = a$ implies $\lim f(s_n) = l$ for every sequence s in $C_S(\{a\})$, then $\lim_{x \to a} f(x) = l$. $\square$

We now have the mapping analog of Theorem 134.

153 THEOREM

Let f and g be mappings of S into $\mathbf{K}$, and let $a \in D(S)$. If $\lim_{x \to a} f(x) = l_1$ and $\lim_{x \to a} g(x) = l_2$, then

[1] $\lim_{x \to a} [f(x) + g(x)] = l_1 + l_2$;

[2] $\lim_{x \to a} c \cdot f(x) = cl_1$ for every $c \in \mathbf{K}$;

[3] $\lim_{x \to a} f(x)g(x) = l_1 \cdot l_2$;

[4] $\lim_{x \to a} \dfrac{f(x)}{g(x)} = \dfrac{l_1}{l_2}$, provided that $l_2 \neq 0$.

Proof

This theorem is an easy and immediate consequence of Theorems 134 and 152. For example, to establish part [1] we observe that if s is any sequence in $C_S(\{a\})$ such that $\lim s_n = a$, then it follows from Theorem 152 that $\lim f(s_n) = l_1$ and $\lim g(s_n) = l_2$. Hence, by Theorem 134, $\lim [f(s_n) + g(s_n)] = l_1 + l_2$. Therefore, it follows from Theorem 152 that $\lim_{x \to a} [f(x) + g(x)] = l_1 + l_2$. The other parts of the theorem can be proved in a similar way. $\square$

The following is typical of a problem that arises frequently in real analysis. Suppose that we wish to calculate

$$\lim_{x \to 2} \frac{x^2 - 4}{x - 2}.$$

Now Theorem 153 cannot be used here, because $\lim_{x \to 2} (x - 2) = 0$. We see, however, that $(x^2 - 4)/(x - 2) = x + 2$ for all $x \neq 2$; and so, since the limit involved depends only on values of the mapping for x near 2 but different from 2, it seems highly likely that

$$\lim_{x \to 2} \frac{x^2 - 4}{x - 2} = \lim_{x \to 2} (x + 2),$$

even though the factor that was cancelled has a limit 0 as x tends to 2. Our next theorem gives assurance that these two limits are indeed the same.

154 THEOREM

Let f and g be mappings of S into $\mathbf{K}$, and let $a \in D(S)$. If there is a neighborhood I of a such that $f(x) = g()x$ for all $x \in C_I(\{a\}) \cap S$, and if $\lim_{x \to a} g(x) = l$, then $\lim_{x \to a} f(x) = l$.

Proof

Let $I =]p, q[$. Since $\lim_{x \to a} g(x) = l$, given $\varepsilon > 0$ there exists $\delta > 0$ such that $|g(x) - l| < \varepsilon$ for all $x \in S$ with $0 < |x - a| < \delta$. Let $\delta_1 = \min\{S, a - p, q - a\}$. If $x \in S$ and $0 < |x - a| < \delta_1$, then $x \in C_I(\{a\}) \cap S$ and $0 < |x - a| < \delta$. Therefore $|f(x) - l| = |g(x) - l| < \varepsilon$, and so $\lim_{x \to a} f(x) = l$. $\square$

The notion of limit of a mapping can be easily generalized to limits from the left and from the right.

155 DEFINITION

Let f be a mapping of a set S into $\mathbf{K}$, and let $a \in \mathbf{K}$. We shall say that the real number l is the *limit of* $f(x)$ *as* x *tends to* a *from the right*, written $\lim_{x \to a^+} f(x) = l$, iff $a \in D(S)$ and for every $\varepsilon > 0$ there exists $\delta_\varepsilon > 0$ such that

$$|f(x) - l| < \varepsilon \quad \text{for all} \quad x \in S \quad \text{with} \quad 0 < x - a < \delta_\varepsilon.$$

Similarly, we shall say that the real number l is the *limit of* $f(x)$ *as* x *tends to* a *from the left*, written $\lim_{x \to a^-} f(x) = l$, iff $a \in D(S)$ and for every $\varepsilon > 0$ there exists $\delta_\varepsilon > 0$ such that

$$|f(x) - l| < \varepsilon \quad \text{for all} \quad x \in S \quad \text{with} \quad 0 < a - x < \delta_\varepsilon.$$

As might be expected, $f(x)$ has a limit as x tends to a if and only if it has the same limit from both the left and right at a.

156 THEOREM

Let f be a mapping of S into $\mathbf{K}$, and let $a \in D(S)$. Then

$$\lim_{x \to a} f(x) = l$$

if and only if

$$\lim_{x \to a^+} f(x) = \lim_{x \to a^-} f(x) = l.$$

(The proof is to be done as an exercise.)

Finally, there are one-sided versions of Theorem 152.

157 THEOREM

Let f be a mapping of S into $\mathbf{K}$, and let $a \in D(S)$. Then

$$\lim_{x \to a^+} f(x) = l$$

if and only if $\lim (s_n) = l$ for every sequence s in $\{x \in S : x > a\}$ such that $\lim s_n = a$. Also, $\lim_{x \to a^-} f(x) = l$ if and only if $\lim f(s_n) = l$ for every sequence s in $\{x \in S : x < a)$ such that $\lim s_n = a$.

(The proof is to be done as an exercise.)

EXERCISES

1 ▷ Prove that if there is a real number c such that $f(x) = c$ for all x in some neighborhood I of a, then $\lim_{x \to a} f(x) = c$.

2 ▷ Prove that $\lim_{x \to a} x = a$ for every $a \in \mathbf{K}$.

3 Use Definition 149 to prove that $\lim_{x \to 2} x^2 = 4$.

4 Use Definition 149 to prove that $\lim_{x \to 1} (x^2 - 3x) = -2$.

5 Use Definition 149 to prove that $\lim_{x \to -2} (2x^2 + 3x) = 2$.

6 Find $\lim_{x \to 0} |x|$.

7 Find $\lim_{x \to 0^+} \dfrac{|x|}{x}$ and $\lim_{x \to 0^-} \dfrac{|x|}{x}$.

8 Prove Theorem 150.

9 Complete the proof of Theorem 153.

10 Prove Theorem 156.

11 Prove Theorem 157.

Continuity

Given a mapping f of S into $\mathbf{K}$, it is not necessary that a actually be a member of S in order to talk about the limit of $f(x)$ as x tends to a. Loosely speaking, $\lim_{x \to a} f(x)$ is completely determined (if it exists at all) by the values of $f(x)$ for x close to a but different from a. Thus, even if a should be a member of S (so that $f(a)$ is defined), it is only by the wildest kind of coincidence that the limit of $f(x)$ as x tends to a turns out to be $f(a)$. It is so much of a coincidence, in fact, that we recognize its occurrence with the following solemn ceremony.

158 DEFINITION

Let f be a mapping of S into $\mathbf{K}$, and let $a \in \mathbf{K}$. The mapping f is said to be *continuous at a* iff

$$a \in S \quad \text{and} \quad \lim_{x \to a} f(x) = f(a).$$

The mapping f is said to be *continuous from the right at a* iff

$$a \in S \quad \text{and} \quad \lim_{x \to a^+} f(x) = f(a).$$

The mapping f is said to be *continuous from the left at a* iff

$$a \in S \quad \text{and} \quad \lim_{x \to a^-} f(x) = f(a).$$

Clearly continuous mappings are nice things to have around the house because of the relative ease with which their limits can be found: To find $\lim_{x \to a} f(x)$—if f is continuous at a—one simply "plugs in" $x = a$.

Our next theorem follows easily from Definition 158 and Theorem 153. The proof is to be done as an exercise.

159 THEOREM

Let f and g be mappings of S into $\mathbf{K}$, and let $a \in S$. If f and g are continuous (continuous from the left, continuous from the right) at a, then

$$f \pm g, cf \quad \text{for every} \quad c \in \mathbf{K}, fg, \text{ and } \frac{f}{g}$$

are also continuous (continuous from the left, continuous from the right, respectively) at a, provided that $g(a) \neq 0$ in the case of f/g.

160 DEFINITION

A mapping f of S into $\mathbf{K}$ is said to be *continuous relative to S* iff f is continuous at each $a \in S$.

For future reference, we shall now identify a rather large class of continuous mappings.

161 THEOREM

If P is a polynomial function, that is if

$$P(x) = a_n x^n + a_{n-1} x^{n-1} + \cdots + a_1 x + a_0$$

where n is a nonnegative integer and $a_i \in \mathbf{K}$ for $i = 0, \ldots, n$, then P is continuous relative to $\mathbf{K}$.

(The proof is to be done as an exercise.)

162 THEOREM

If R is a rational function, that is if

$$R(x) = \frac{P(x)}{Q(x)}$$

where P and Q are polynomial functions, and if a is any real number for which $Q(a) \neq 0$, then R is continuous at a.

Proof

Theorems 161 and 159. $\square$

EXERCISES

1   Find each of the following.

(a) $\lim\limits_{x \to 2} \dfrac{x^2 - 25}{x - 5}$.

(b) $\lim\limits_{x \to 5} \dfrac{x^2 - 25}{x - 5}$.

(c) $\lim\limits_{x \to 0} \dfrac{(3 + x)^2 - 9}{x}$.

(d) $\lim\limits_{x \to 3} \dfrac{x^3 - 27}{x - 3}$.

(e) $\lim\limits_{x \to -3} (|x|^2 - 4|x|)$.

(f) $\lim\limits_{x \to 0} \left(\dfrac{x}{|x|} \right) \left(\dfrac{|x|}{x} \right)$.

2   ▷ Let f be a mapping of S into $\mathbf{K}$, and let $a \in \mathbf{K}$. Prove that f is continuous at a if and only if f is continuous from the left and from the right at a.

3   ▷ Let f be a mapping of S into $\mathbf{K}$ and let $a \in \mathbf{K}$. Prove that f is continuous at a if and only if $a \in S \cap D(S)$ and for every $\varepsilon > 0$ there exists $\delta_\varepsilon > 0$ such that $|f(x) - f(a)| < \varepsilon$ for all $x \in S$ with $|x - a| < \delta_\varepsilon$.

4   Prove Theorem 159.

5   Prove Theorem 161. [Hint: Use Theorem 153 with Exercises 1 and 2 on page 103.]

6   Discuss continuity of each of the following mappings.

(a) $f(x) = \begin{cases} \dfrac{x^2 - 1}{x - 1}, & x \neq 1 \\ 2, & x = 1. \end{cases}$

(b) $g(x) = \begin{cases} 2^{1/x}, & x \neq 0 \\ 0, & x = 0. \end{cases}$

(c) $h(x) = \begin{cases} \dfrac{(3 + x)^2 - 9}{x}, & x \neq 0 \\ 6, & x = 0. \end{cases}$

(d) $g(x) = \begin{cases} \dfrac{|x|}{x}, & x \neq 0 \\ 1, & x = 0. \end{cases}$

7 ▷ Let f and g be mappings of a set S into **K**, and let $a \in D(S)$. Prove that if $\lim_{x \to a} f(x) = 0$, and if there exists a neighborhood I of a such that $|g(x)| \leq |f(x)|$ for every $x \in C_I(\{a\}) \cap S$, then $\lim_{x \to a} g(x) = 0$.

8 ▷ Let f be a mapping of S into **K**, and let $a \in D(S)$. Prove that if there exists a mapping h of S into S such that

$$0 < |h(x) - a| < |x - a|$$

for every $x \in S$ with $x \neq a$, and if $\lim_{x \to a} f(x) = l$, then $\lim_{x \to a} f(h(x)) = l$.

9   Generalize the theorem in Exercise 7 above to limits from the left and right.

Basic Properties of Continuous Mappings

In much of our work to follow we shall confine our attention to continuous mappings. One reason for so doing has already been mentioned, namely the relative ease with which limits of such mappings can be handled. A second reason is that mappings that are continuous at each point of a closed interval behave themselves very nicely with respect to that interval. What "very nicely" means will soon be made clear. First, however, we need some more terminology.

163 DEFINITION

Let f be a mapping of S into $\mathbf{K}$ and let I be any interval. We shall say that f is a *function defined over the interval* I iff $I \subset S$. A function f defined over an open interval $]a, b[$ is said to be *continuous over* $]a, b[$ iff f is continuous at each point of $]a, b[$. A function f defined over a closed interval $[a, b]$ is said to be *continuous over* $[a, b]$ iff f is continuous at each point of $]a, b[$, continuous from the right at a, and continuous from the left at b. A function f defined over an interval I is said to be *bounded over* I iff there exist real numbers l and u such that

$$l \leq f(x) \leq u \qquad \text{for every} \quad x \in I.$$

Now we turn to those "very nice" properties.

164 THEOREM Boundedness Theorem

If f is defined and continuous over a closed interval $[a, b]$, then f is bounded over $[a, b]$.

Proof

For each $p \in]a, b[$,

$$\lim_{x \to p} f(x) = f(p).$$

Hence (using Exercise 3, p. 105 with $\varepsilon = 1$) there exists $\delta_p^{\bullet} > 0$ such that

$$|f(x) - f(p)| < 1 \qquad \text{for all} \quad x \in [a, b], \quad \text{with} \quad |x - p| < \delta_p^{\bullet}.$$

Hence there exists $\delta_p > 0$ such that

$$|f(x) - f(p)| < 1 \qquad \text{for all} \quad x, \quad \text{with} \quad |x - p| < \delta_p$$

(specifically take $\delta_p = \min\{\delta_p^{\bullet}, p - a, b - p\}$).
  Let $N_p =]p - \delta_p, p + \delta_p[$. Then

$$|f(x) - f(p)| < 1 \qquad \text{for all} \quad x \in N_p.$$

Also $\lim_{x \to a^+} f(x) = f(a)$. Hence there exists $\delta_a > 0$ such that

$$|f(x) - f(a)| < 1 \qquad \text{for all} \quad x, \quad \text{with} \quad x - a < \delta a.$$

Let $N_a =]a - \delta_a, a + \delta_a[$. Then

$$|f(x) - f(a)| < 1 \qquad \text{for all} \quad x \in N_a \cap [a, b].$$

Finally, $\lim_{x \to b^-} f(x) = f(b)$. Hence there exists $\delta_b > 0$ such that

$$|f(x) - f(b)| < 1 \qquad \text{for all} \quad x, \quad \text{with} \quad b - x < \delta_b.$$

Let $N_b = \,]b - \delta_b, b + \delta_b[$. Then

$$|f(x) - f(b)| < 1 \qquad \text{for all} \quad x \in N_b \cap [a, b].$$

Now $\{N_p : p \in [a, b]\}$ is an open covering of $[a, b]$. Since $[a, b]$ is compact, there exist a finite number of points in $[a, b]$, say $p_1, \ldots, p_n$, such that $\{N_{p_1}, \ldots, N_{p_n}\}$ is a covering of $[a, b]$. Let

$$u = (\max\{f(p_1), \ldots, f(p_n)\}) + 1$$

and let

$$l = (\min\{f(p_1), \ldots, f(p_n)\}) - 1.$$

If $x \in [a, b]$, then $x \in N_{p_i}$ for some i, and so

$$|f(x) - f(p_i)| < 1.$$

Hence

$$-1 < f(x) - f(p_i) < 1,$$

so

$$f(p_i) - 1 < f(x) < (p_i) + 1$$

But $f(p_i) + 1 \le u$ and $f(p_i) - 1 \ge l$. Hence $u \le f(x) \le l$ for every $x \in [a, b]$. Therefore f is bounded over $[a, b]$. $\square$

165 THEOREM   Min-Max Theorem

If f is defined and continuous over a closed interval $[a, b]$, then there exist $x_1 \in [a, b]$ and $x_2 \in [a, b]$ such that

$$f(x_1) \le f(x) \le f(x_2) \qquad \text{for every} \quad x \in [a, b].$$

Proof

According to the boundedness theorem, the set

$$Y = \{f(x) : x \in [a, b]\}$$

is bounded above and below. Also $f(a) \in Y$, so $Y \ne \varnothing$. Let u be the least upper bound of Y, and let l be the greatest lower bound of Y. Then

$$l \le f(x) \le u \qquad \text{for all} \quad x \in [a, b].$$

We shall now show that there exists $x_2 \in [a, b]$ such that $f(x_2) = u$. The proof that there exists $x_1 \in [a, b]$ such that $f(x_1) = l$ is similar and is left as an exercise.

Assume that there is no $x_2 \in [a, b]$ such that $f(x_2) = u$. Then $f(x) < u$ for every $x \in [a, b]$. Therefore $u - f(x) > 0$ for every $x \in [a, b]$. Hence the function g defined by

$$g(x) = \frac{1}{u - f(x)}$$

is defined and continuous over $[a, b]$ (Theorem 159). By the boundedness theorem, then, there exists $d > 0$ such that

$$\frac{1}{u - f(x)} \le d \qquad \text{for every} \quad x \in [a, b].$$

Then

$$1 \le d(u - f(x)),$$

$$df(x) \le du - 1,$$

$$f(x) \le u - 1/d < u \qquad \text{for every} \quad x \in [a, b].$$

Thus $u - (1/d)$ is an upper bound of Y that is smaller than the least upper bound of Y. This contradiction implies that there exists $x_2 \in [a, b]$ such that $f(x_2) = u$. $\square$

166 THEOREM   Intermediate Value Theorem

If f is defined and continuous over a closed interval $[a, b]$, and if $f(a) \neq f(b)$, then for every real number r between† $f(a)$ and $f(b)$, there exists $x_r \in \,]a, b[$ such that $f(x_r) = r$.

Proof

Since $f(a) \neq f(b)$, either $f(a) < f(b)$ or $f(a) > f(b)$. We shall consider the case in which $f(a) < f(b)$; the proof in case $f(a) > f(b)$ is similar and is left as an exercise.

Let r be any real number for which $f(a) < r < f(b)$. Let x_1 be the midpoint of $[a, b]$. If $f(x_1) = r$, then we are done. If not, then either $f(x_1) > r$ or $f(x_1) < r$. Let

$$[a_1, b_1] = \begin{cases} [a, x_1] & \text{if} \quad f(x_1) > r \\ [x_1, b] & \text{if} \quad f(x_1) < r. \end{cases}$$

† We shall say that γ is *between* α and β iff $\alpha \neq \beta$ and either $\alpha < \gamma < \beta$ or $\beta < \gamma < \alpha$.

Then $[a_1, b_1] \subset [a, b]$,

$$b_1 - a_1 = \tfrac{1}{2}(b - a),$$

and $f(a_1) < r < f(b_1)$.

Now assume that intervals $[a_1, b_1], [a_2, b_2], \ldots, [a_n, b_n]$ have been chosen so that

$$[a_n, b_n] \subset [a_{n-1}, b_{n-1}] \subset \cdots \subset [a_1, b_1] \subset [a, b],$$

$$b_i - a_i = \frac{1}{2^i}(b - a) \qquad i = 1, \ldots, n,$$

and

$$f(a_i) < r < f(b_i) \qquad i = 1, \ldots, n.$$

Let x_{n+1} be the midpoint of $[a_n, b_n]$. If $f(x_{n+1}) = r$, then we are done. If not, then either

$$f(x_{n+1}) > r \quad \text{or} \quad f(x_{n+1}) < r.$$

Let

$$[a_{n+1}, b_{n+1}] = \begin{cases} [a_n, x_{n+1}] & \text{if } f(x_{n+1}) > r \\ [x_{n+1}, b_n] & \text{if } f(x_{n+1}) < r. \end{cases}$$

Then $[a_{n+1}, b_{n+1}] \subset [a_n, b_n]$,

$$b_{n+1} - a_{n+1} = \tfrac{1}{2}(b_n - a_n) = \frac{1}{2^{n+1}}(b - a),$$

and $f(a_{n+1}) < r < f(b_{n+1})$.

Hence, by induction, either $f(x_n) = r$ for some $n \in \mathbf{N}$, in which case we are done, or else we have a sequence of closed intervals $[a_n, b_n]$ such that

$$[a_{n+1}, b_{n+1}] \subset [a_n, b_n] \qquad \text{for every} \quad n \in \mathbf{N},$$
$$f(a_n) < r < f(b_n) \qquad \text{for every} \quad n \in \mathbf{N},$$

and

$$\lim(b_n - a_n) = (b - a)\lim \frac{1}{2^n} = 0.$$

By the nested interval theorem there exists a unique $x_0 \in \mathbf{K}$ such that

$$x_0 \in [a_n, b_n] \qquad \text{for every} \quad n \in \mathbf{N}.$$

Given $\varepsilon > 0$, choose n_ε so that $1/2^{n_\varepsilon} < \varepsilon/(b - a)$ (this can be done since, by Theorem 135, $\lim 1/2^n = 0$). If $n \geq n_\varepsilon$, then

$$|a_n - x_0| \leq b_n - a_n = \frac{1}{2^n}(b - a) \leq \frac{1}{2^n}(b - a) < \varepsilon,$$

and $|b_n - x_0| \leq b_n - a_n < \varepsilon$. Hence $\lim a_n = \lim b_n = x_0$. Since f is continuous at x_0, $f(x_0) = \lim f(a_n) = \lim f(b_n)$. But $f(a_n) < r$ and $f(b_n) > r$ for every $n \in \mathbf{N}$. Therefore (see Exercise 6, p. 82), $\lim f(a_n) \leq r$ and $\lim f(b_n) \geq r$. Hence $f(x_0) \leq r$ and $f(x_0) \geq r$, from which it follows that $f(x_0) = r$.

Since $x_0 \in [a_1, b_1] \subset [a, b]$, it follows that $x_0 \in [a, b]$. But $f(x_0) = r$, $r \neq f(a)$, and $r \neq f(b)$. Therefore $x_0 \neq a$ and $x_0 \neq b$. Hence $x_0 \in \,]a, b[$. $\square$

EXERCISES

1   Give an example showing that a function that is defined and continuous over an open interval need not be bounded over that interval.

2   Give an example showing that a function that is defined, continuous, and bounded over an open interval need not have a maximum or a minimum value over that interval.

3   Give an example of a function defined over a closed interval that does not have the intermediate value property.

4   Prove that if P is a polynomial function and a and b are real numbers such that $P(a) \cdot P(b) < 0$, then there is a real number x_0 between a and b such that x_0 is a root of the equation $P(x) = 0$.

5   Use Exercise 4 above to prove that there exists a positive real number r such that $r^2 = \pi$.

6   If $f(x) = x^2 + 2x + 2$ and $[a, b] = [-2, 2]$, find the numbers x_1 and x_2 whose existence is guaranteed by the min-max theorem.

7   Complete the proof of Theorem 165.

8   Complete the proof of Theorem 166.

☰ THE DERIVATIVE

It is assumed that the reader has had some previous exposure to the concept of the derivative of a function. In particular, little attention will be given here to the interpretation of the derivative as the slope of a tangent line, the interpretation of the derivative as a rate of change, and the manipulative techniques of formal differentiation. Instead, emphasis will be given to the theoretical considerations that underlie the rules and procedures of the differential calculus.

In the remote event that the reader has experienced an erosion of his knowledge of basic calculus, he might find a review of the subject in order before proceeding with this chapter.

Definition and Fundamental Properties

167 DEFINITION

Let f be defined over a neighborhood of the real number a. If there exists a real number l such that

$$\lim_{h \to 0} \frac{f(a + h) - f(a)}{h} = l$$

then we shall say that f is *differentiable* at a and that l is the *derivative* of f at a. If no such real number l exists, then we shall say that f is *not differentiable* at a, or that f has no derivative at a. We shall say that f is *differentiable over a set* $S \subset \mathbf{K}$ iff f is differentiable at each point of S.

In order to illustrate the concept of Definition 167, consider the function f defined by $f(x) = x^2$.

We have

$$\lim_{h \to 0} \frac{(2 + h)^2 - 2^2}{h} = \lim_{h \to 0} (4 + h) = 4$$

and so f is differentiable at 2, and its derivative at 2 is 4. More generally, for fixed but arbitrary $x \in \mathbf{K}$,

$$\lim_{h \to 0} \frac{(x + h)^2 - x^2}{h} = \lim_{h \to 0} (2x + h) = 2x.$$

Hence f is differentiable at every $x \in \mathbf{K}$ and its derivative at x is $2x$. Also f is differentiable over $\mathbf{K}$.

As another example, consider the function g defined by $g(x) = |x|$. Note that

$$\frac{g(h) - g(0)}{h} = \frac{|h|}{h}$$

and so

$$\lim_{h \to 0^+} \frac{g(h) - g(0)}{h} = \lim_{h \to 0^+} \frac{h}{h} = 1,$$

while

$$\lim_{h \to 0^-} \frac{g(h) - g(0)}{h} = \lim_{h \to 0^-} -\frac{h}{h} = -1.$$

It follows that

$$\lim_{h \to 0} \frac{g(h) - g(0)}{h}$$

does not exist, and so g is not differentiable at 0. For fixed but arbitrary $x > 0$,

$$\lim_{h \to 0} \frac{g(x + h) - g(x)}{h} = \lim_{h \to 0} \frac{(x + h) - x}{h} = 1,$$

while for fixed but arbitrary $x < 0$,

$$\lim_{h \to 0} \frac{g(x + h) - g(x)}{h} = \lim_{h \to 0} - \frac{(x + h) - (-x)}{h} = -1.$$

Hence g is differentiable at every $x \neq 0$, so g is differentiable over $C_{\mathbf{K}}(\{0\})$.

168 DEFINITION

For a given mapping f of S into $\mathbf{K}$, $S \subset \mathbf{K}$, let M be the set of all real numbers at which f is differentiable. If $M = \varnothing$ then we shall say that f *has no derivative*. If $M \neq \varnothing$ then the function f' with domain M defined by

$$f'(x) = \lim_{h \to 0} \frac{f(x + h) - f(x)}{h}$$

is called the *derivative of f*.

In the two examples above,

$$f'(x) = 2x,$$

and

$$g'(x) = \begin{cases} 1, & x > 0 \\ -1, & x < 0. \end{cases}$$

Continuity and differentiability at a point are related, with the latter being the stronger condition.

169 THEOREM

If f is differentiable at the real number a, then f is continuous at a.

Proof

Since f is differentiable at a, there exists a real number l such that

$$\lim_{h \to 0} \frac{f(a + h) - f(a)}{h} = l.$$

Now consider

$$\lim_{x \to a} \frac{f(x) - f(a)}{x - a}.$$

Setting $x = a + h$ we have

$$\lim_{x \to a} \frac{f(x) - f(a)}{x - a} = \lim_{h \to 0} \frac{f(a + h) - f(a)}{h} = l$$

(since $0 < |x - a| < \delta$ implies $0 < |h| < \delta$). Hence there exists $\delta_0 > 0$ such that

$$\left| \frac{f(x) - f(a)}{x - a} - l \right| < 1 \qquad \text{for all} \quad x \quad \text{with} \quad 0 < |x - a| < \delta_0.$$

Therefore, if $0 < |x - a| < \delta_0$, then

$$-1 < \frac{f(x) - f(a)}{x - a} - l < 1,$$

so

$$l - 1 < \frac{f(x) - f(a)}{x - a} < l + 1.$$

Set $M = \max \{|l + 1|, |l - 1|\}$. Then $M > 0$ (since $l + 1$ and $l - 1$ can't both be 0), and

$$\left| \frac{f(x) - f(a)}{x - a} \right| < M \qquad \text{for all} \quad x, \quad \text{with} \quad 0 < |x - a| < \delta_0.$$

Given $\varepsilon > 0$, let $\delta = \min \{\delta_0, \varepsilon/M\}$. If $0 < |x - a| < \delta$, then

$$|f(x) - f(a)| = \left| \frac{f(x) - f(a)}{x - a} \right| |x - a| < M\delta \leq M \frac{\varepsilon}{M} = \varepsilon.$$

Therefore $\lim_{x \to a} f(x) = f(a)$, and so f is continuous at a. $\square$

Note that the function given by $g(x) = |x|$ is continuous at 0 but is not differentiable there. Consequently the converse of Theorem 169 is false.

We conclude this section with a theorem that is very useful in applications of the differential calculus to problems involving maximum and/or minimum values of a function.

170 THEOREM

If f is differentiable at x_1, and if $f(x) \geq f(x_1)$ for all x in some neighborhood of x_1, then $f(x_1) = 0$. Similarly, if f is differentiable at x_2, and if $f(x) \leq f(x_2)$ for all x in some neighborhood of x_2, then $f'(x_2) = 0$.

Proof

Assume that f is differentiable at x_1 and that $f(x) \geq f(x_1)$ for all x in some neighborhood of x_1. Then

$$\lim_{h \to 0} \frac{f(x_1 + h) - f(x_1)}{h}$$

exists, so both

$$\lim_{h \to 0^+} \frac{f(x_1 + h) - f(x_1)}{h}$$

and

$$\lim_{h \to 0^-} \frac{f(x_1 + h) - f(x_1)}{h}$$

exist and are equal to $f'(x_1)$.

But

$$\frac{f(x_1 + h) - f(x_1)}{h} \geq 0$$

for all sufficiently small positive h, since $f(x) \geq f(x_1)$ for all x in some neighborhood of x_1. For the same reason,

$$\frac{f(x_1 + h) - f(x_1)}{h} \leq 0$$

for all negative h of sufficiently small absolute value. Hence

$$f'(x_1) = \lim_{h \to 0^+} \frac{f(x_1 + h) - f(x_1)}{h} \geq 0$$

and

$$f'(x_1) = \lim_{h \to 0^-} \frac{f(x_1 + h) - f(x_1)}{h} \leq 0.$$

Therefore

$$f'(x_1) = 0.$$

The proof of the second assertion of the theorem is left as an exercise. $\square$

EXERCISES

1 ▷ Prove that if f and g are differentiable at a, then $f \pm g$ is differentiable at a and

$$(f \pm g)'(a) = f'(a) \pm g'(a).$$

2   Prove that if f and g are differentiable at a, then fg is differentiable at a and

$$(fg)'(a) = f(a)g'(a) + f'(a)g(a).$$

3 ▷ Prove that if P is a polynomial function, that is, if

$$P(x) = a_n x^n + \cdots + a_1 x + a_0, \qquad n \geq 0,$$

then

$$P'(x) = na_n x^{n-1} + \cdots + a_1.$$

Hence every polynomial function is differentiable over $\mathbf{K}$, and the derivative of a polynomial function is a polynomial function.

4   Consider the function f defined by

$$f(x) = x^{2/3}.$$

(a) Show that $f(x) \geq 0$ for every $x \in \mathbf{K}$.
(b) Show that f is not differentiable at 0.
(c) Do (a) and (b) contradict Theorem 170? Explain.

5   Complete the proof of Theorem 170.

The Mean Value Theorem

If one considers a nice, smooth curve and selects on it two distinct points, there is good intuitive reason to suspect that there is at least one point on the curve, between the two selected, at which the tangent line is parallel to the line on the two selected points. As believable as this fact is, it turns out to be a fairly deep piece of mathematics, depending on essentially everything that has been presented up to now in this book. It is, moreover, an extremely important piece of mathematics; if one were to be shipwrecked on a desert isle, he could do far worse than take this fact (which is called the *mean value theorem*) with him—especially if he plans to do a theoretical development of the calculus in his spare time.

We shall first establish a special case of the mean value theorem.

171 THEOREM   Rolle's Theorem

If f is continuous over $[a, b]$ and differentiable over $]a, b[$, and if $f(a) = f(b)$, then there exists $x_0 \in]a, b[$ such that $f'(x_0) = 0$.

Proof

By the min-max theorem (Theorem 165), there exist x_1 and x_2 in $[a, b]$ such that

$$f(x_1) \leq f(x) \leq f(x_2) \qquad \text{for every} \quad x \in [a, b].$$

If $x_1 = a$ and $x_2 = b$, or if $x_1 = b$ and $x_2 = a$, then, since $f(a) = f(b)$, we have

$$f(x) = k \qquad \text{for every} \quad x \in [a, b]$$

where $k = f(a) = f(b)$. Let

$$x_0 = \tfrac{1}{2}(a + b).$$

Then

$$f'(x_0) = \lim_{h \to 0} \frac{f(x_0 + h) - f(x_0)}{h}$$

$$= \lim_{h \to 0} \frac{k - k}{h}$$

$$= \lim_{h \to 0} 0 = 0$$

The only other possibilities are that $x_1 \in \,]a, b[$, in which case $f'(x_1) = 0$ by Theorem 170; or else $x_2 \in \,]a, b[$, in which case $f'(x_2) = 0$. $\square$

172 THEOREM   Mean Value Theorem for Derivatives

If f is continuous over $[a, b]$ and differentiable over $]a, b[$, then there exists $x_0 \in \,]a, b[$ such that

$$f'(x_0) = \frac{f(b) - f(a)}{b - a}.$$

Proof

Let

$$F(x) = f(x) - \frac{f(b) - f(a)}{b - a} x.$$

Then F is continuous over $[a, b]$ (Theorems 161 and 159). Moreover F is differentiable over $]a, b[$ and

$$F'(x) = f'(x) - \frac{f(b) - f(a)}{b - a}$$

(Exercises 1 and 3, p. 117). Now

$$F(a) = \frac{bf(a) - af(b)}{b - a},$$

and

$$F(b) = \frac{bf(a) - af(b)}{b - a} = F(a).$$

Hence, by Rolle's theorem, there exists $x_0 \in \,]a, b[$ such that $F'(x_0) = 0$. Hence

$$f'(x_0) - \frac{f(b) - f(a)}{b - a} = 0,$$

and the theorem follows. □

As our first application of the mean value theorem, we shall establish a sufficient but not-quite-necessary condition that a differentiable function be increasing (or decreasing) over an interval.

173 DEFINITION

A function f defined over an open interval I is said to be *increasing over* I iff

$$f(x_1) < f(x_2)$$

whenever x_1 and x_2 are both in I and $x_1 < x_2$. The function f is said to be *decreasing over* I iff

$$f(x_1) > f(x_2)$$

whenever x_1 and x_2 are both in I and $x_1 < x_2$.

174 THEOREM

If f is differentiable over $]a, b[$, and if f is increasing (decreasing) over $]a, b[$, then $f'(x) \geq 0$ (resp. $f'(x) \leq 0$) for all $x \in \,]a, b[$.

Proof

Assume that f is differentiable over $]a, b[$ and that f is increasing over $]a, b[$. Let x be any point of $]a, b[$. Then

$$\frac{f(x + h) - f(x)}{h} > 0$$

for every $h \neq 0$ and sufficiently small that $(x + h) \in \,]a, b[$. Hence

$$f'(x) = \lim_{h \to 0} \frac{f(x+h) - f(x)}{h} \geq 0.$$

The proof in case f is decreasing over $]a, b[$ is left as an exercise. □

Theorem 174 is the best possible theorem of its type, in the sense that it is not possible to conclude under the stated conditions that $f'(x)$ is strictly positive for every $x \in]a, b[$. For example consider

$$f(x) = x^3.$$

It is true that f is differentiable and increasing over $]-1, 1[$, but $f'(0) = 0$.

175 THEOREM

If f is differentiable over $]a, b[$, and if $f'(x) > 0 (f'(x) < 0)$ for every $x \in]a, b[$, then f is increasing (resp. decreasing) over $]a, b[$.

Proof

Assume that f is differentiable over $]a, b[$ and that $f'(x) > 0$ for every $x \in]a, b[$. Let x_1 and x_2 be any two points of $]a, b[$ with $x_1 < x_2$. Then

$$[x_1, x_2] \subset]a, b[,$$

and so f is continuous over $[x_1, x_2]$ (Theorem 169). Hence, by the mean value theorem, there exists $x_0 \in]x_1, x_2[$ such that

$$f'(x_0) = \frac{f(x_2) - f(x_1)}{x_2 - x_1}.$$

But $f'(x) > 0$ for every $x \in]a, b[$, so $f'(x_0) > 0$. Hence

$$\frac{f(x_2) - f(x_1)}{x_2 - x_1} > 0.$$

Since $x_2 > x_1$, it follows that $f(x_2) > f(x_1)$. Therefore f is increasing over $]a, b[$.

The proof of the second assertion will again be left as an exercise. □

EXERCISES

1   Give an example to show that Rolle's theorem is no longer true if the hypothesis that f be differentiable over $]a, b[$ is deleted.

2   Complete the proof of Theorem 174.

3   Complete the proof of Theorem 175.

4　A point $(a, f(a))$ is said to be a *relative maximum* of a function f iff $f(x) \leq f(a)$ for all x in the intersection with the domain of f of some neighborhood of a. Similarly, $(a, f(a))$ is said to be a *relative minimum* of f iff $f(x) \geq f(a)$ for all x in the intersection with the domain of f of some neighborhood of a. A point $(a, f(a))$ is an *absolute maximum* (*absolute minimum*) of f iff $f(x) \leq f(a)$ (resp. $f(x) \geq f(a)$) for all x in the domain of f. An *extreme point* of a function is a point that is either a relative maximum, relative minimum, absolute maximum, or absolute minimum.

Discuss a procedure (based on Theorems 170 and 175) for finding and classifying all the extreme points of a function.

5　Find and classify all extreme points of $f(x) = (1 - x^2)^{1/2}$ given that

$$f'(x) = -x(1 - x^2)^{-1/2}.$$

6　Find and classify all extreme points of $f(x) = x^{3/2}$ given that

$$f'(x) = \tfrac{3}{2}x^{1/2}.$$

7　Find and classify all extreme points of

$$f(x) = 6x^{2/3} - 4x,$$

given that

$$f'(x) = 4(1 - x^{1/3})x^{-1/3}.$$

Some Odds and Ends

It is quite easy to show that if a function is constant over some interval, then its derivative is zero over the interior of that interval; the argument consists mainly of the observation that

$$f(x + h) - f(x) = 0$$

for $|h|$ sufficiently small. The converse assertion is also true, but, since its proof involves the mean value theorem, the converse does not lie quite so near the surface.

176 THEOREM

If f is continuous over $[a, b]$ and differentiable over $]a, b[$, and if $f'(x) = 0$

for every $x \in \,]a, b[$, then there exists $k \in K$ such that $f(x) = k$ for every $x \in [a, b]$.

Proof

Let $k = f(a)$. If $x \in \,]a, b]$, then, by the mean value theorem, there exists $x_0 \in \,]a, x[$ such that

$$\frac{f(x) - f(a)}{x - a} = f'(x_0).$$

But $f'(x_0) = 0$, so

$$f(x) = f(a) = k \qquad \text{for every} \quad x \in \,]a, b].$$

Therefore

$$f(x) = k \qquad \text{for every} \quad x \in [a, b]. \quad \square$$

An easy consequence of Theorem 176 is the fact that two functions with the same derivative differ by at most a constant.

177 THEOREM

If f and g are continuous over $[a, b]$ and differentiable over $]a, b[$, and if $f'(x) = g'(x)$ for every $x \in \,]a, b[$, then there exists $k \in K$ such that

$$f(x) = g(x) + k.$$

Proof

Let $H(x) = f(x) - g(x)$. Then H is continuous over $[a, b]$ and differentiable over $]a, b[$. Moreover

$$H'(x) = f'(x) - g'(x) = 0$$

for every $x \in \,]a, b[$. Therefore, there exists $k \in K$ such that $H(x) = k$ for every $x \in [a, b]$. Hence

$$f(x) - g(x) = k \qquad \text{for every} \quad x \in [a, b],$$

and so

$$f(x) = g(x) + k \qquad \text{for every} \quad x \in [a, b]. \quad \square$$

We conclude this chapter with a theorem of considerable practical significance in the computation of derivatives.

178 THEOREM   Chain Rule

If g is differentiable at a and f is differentiable at $g(a)$, then

$$(f(g))'(a) = f'(g(a))g'(a).$$

Proof

$$(f(g))'(a) = \lim_{h \to 0} \frac{f(g(a + h)) - f(g(a))}{h}.$$

Let $\alpha = g(a)$ and $z = g(a + h) - g(a)$, so that

$$g(a + h) = z + g(a) = z + \alpha.$$

We then have

$$(f(g))'(a) = \lim_{h \to 0} \frac{f(\alpha + z) - f(\alpha)}{h}.$$

Now let

$$\varphi(z) = \begin{cases} \dfrac{f(\alpha + z) - f(\alpha)}{z} - f'(\alpha), & z \neq 0 \\[2mm] 0, & z = 0. \end{cases}$$

Then

$$\frac{f(\alpha + z) - f(\alpha)}{h} = \frac{z}{h} f'(\alpha) + \frac{z}{h} \varphi(z)$$

for every $h \neq 0$. Therefore

$$(f(g))'(\alpha) = \lim_{h \to 0} \left[\frac{z}{h} f'(\alpha) + \frac{z}{h} \varphi(z) \right]$$

$$= \lim_{h \to 0} \frac{z}{h} \lim_{h \to 0} [f'(\alpha) + \varphi(z)]$$

$$= \lim_{h \to 0} \frac{g(a + h) - g(a)}{h} \lim_{h \to 0} [f'(\alpha) + \varphi(z)]$$

$$= g'(a) [f'(\alpha) + \lim_{z \to 0} \varphi(z)]$$

$$= g'(a) f'(\alpha)$$

$$= g'(a) f'(g(a)). \quad \square$$

EXERCISES

1   Given that if $f(x) = x^2$ and $g(x) = \sin x$, then $f'(x) = 2x$ and $g'(x) = \cos x$, find $h'(x)$ if $h(x) = \sin^2 x$.

2   Given that if $f(x) = \log x$ and $g(x) = \cos 2x$, then $f'(x) = 1/x$ and $g'(x) = -2 \sin 2x$, find $h'(x)$ if $h(x) = \log(\cos 2x)$.

3   Prove that if f is continuous over $[a, a + c]$, $c > 0$, and differentiable over $]a, a + c[$, then there exists $\theta \in]0, 1[$ such that

$$f(a + c) = f(a) + cf'(a + \theta c).$$

4   Prove that if f is differentiable at a, then

$$\lim_{h \to 0} \frac{f(a + h) - f(a - h)}{h} = 2f'(a).$$

5   Let f and g be continuous over $[a, b]$ and differentiable over $]a, b[$. Prove that if $g(a) \neq g(b)$ and

$$[f'(x)]^2 + [g'(x)]^2 \neq 0 \qquad \text{for all} \quad x \in]a, b[,$$

then there is a number $x_0 \in]a, b[$ such that

$$\frac{f(b) - f(a)}{g(b) - g(a)} = \frac{f'(x_0)}{g'(x_0)}.$$

[Hint: Consider the function H defined by

$$H(x) = f(x) - f(a) - \frac{f(b) - f(a)}{g(b) - g(a)}(g(x) - g(a)).]$$

6   *L'Hospital's Rule*   Let f and g be differentiable over the set

$$S =]\alpha, a[\cup]a, \beta[, \qquad \alpha < a < \beta,$$

and let both $g(x)$ and $g'(x)$ be different from 0 for all $x \in S$. Prove that if

$$\lim_{x \to a} f(x) = \lim_{x \to a} g(x) = 0,$$

and if

$$\lim_{x \to a} \frac{f'(x)}{g'(x)}$$

exists, then

$$\lim_{x \to a} \frac{f(x)}{g(x)} = \lim_{x \to a} \frac{f'(x)}{g'(x)}.$$

[Hint: Use the result of Exercise 5.]

THE RIEMANN
IV THEORY OF
INTEGRATION

It is again assumed that the reader has had previous exposure to the basic notions of the calculus, and, in particular, that he is familiar with the standard interpretation of the integral as an area. It is also assumed that the reader either knows or can quickly recall the fundamentals of formal integration. In any event, little attention will be given here to such matters. Instead, we shall mainly be concerned with the theoretical considerations that form the basis of the integral calculus.

Fundamental Definitions

In order to give a reasonably concise definition of the Riemann integral it is necessary to introduce a few technical terms.

127

179 DEFINITION

A *partition* P of a closed interval $[a, b]$ is a finite set of points

$$P = \{x_0, x_1, \ldots, x_n\}, \qquad n \geq 1,$$

such that

$$a = x_0 < x_1 < \cdots < x_n = b.$$

If P is a partition of $[a, b]$, then for each $i = 1, \ldots, n$ we define $\Delta_i x$ by

$$\Delta_i x = x_i - x_{i-1}.$$

The *norm* of P, denoted by $|P|$, is defined by

$$|P| = \max \{\Delta_1 x, \Delta_2 x, \ldots, \Delta_n x\}.$$

If P_1 and P_2 are partitions of $[a, b]$, we shall say that P_1 is *finer than* P_2, or that P_1 is a *refinement* of P_2, iff $P_1 \supset P_2$.

For example, if

$$P = \{0, \tfrac{1}{4}, \tfrac{1}{2}, 1\},$$

then P is a partition of $[0, 1]$, and we have

$$\Delta_1 x = \tfrac{1}{4}, \Delta_2 x = \tfrac{1}{4}, \Delta_3 x = \tfrac{1}{2},$$

and so

$$|P| = \tfrac{1}{2}.$$

If $P = \{0, 3, 5, 5\tfrac{1}{2}, 5\tfrac{3}{4}, 6\}$, then P is a partition of $[0, 6]$ with

$$\Delta_1 x = 3, \Delta_2 x = 2, \Delta_3 x = \tfrac{1}{2}, \Delta_4 x = \Delta_5 x = \tfrac{1}{4},$$

and so $|P| = 3$. If $P_1 = \{0, 1, 3, 5, 5\tfrac{1}{2}, 5\tfrac{3}{4}, 6\}$, then P_1 is finer than P, since $P_1 \supset P$.

180 DEFINITION

Let $P = \{x_0, x_1, \ldots, x_n\}$ be a partition of $[a, b]$. A mapping c of $\{1, 2, \ldots, n\}$ into $[a, b]$ is called a *choice function associated with* P iff

$$c(i) \in [x_{i-1}, x_i] \qquad \text{for every} \quad i = 1, \ldots, n.$$

As an example, if $P = \{1, 1\tfrac{1}{4}, 1\tfrac{3}{4}, 2\}$ and c is defined by

$$c(1) = 1, c(2) = 1\tfrac{1}{2}, c(3) = 2,$$

then c is a choice function associated with P.

If $P = \{3, 3\tfrac{1}{4}, 3\tfrac{1}{2}, 3\tfrac{3}{4}, 4\}$, and c is defined by $c(1) = 3\tfrac{1}{8}, c(2) = 3\tfrac{5}{8}$, $c(3) = 3\tfrac{5}{8}, c(4) = 3\tfrac{3}{4}$, then c is a choice function associated with P.

181 DEFINITION

Let f be a function defined over $[a, b]$, let $P = \{x_0, x_1, \ldots, x_n\}$ be a partition of $[a, b]$, and let c be a choice function associated with P. The *Riemann sum* $S(f; P, c)$ is defined by

$$S(f; P, c) = \sum_{i=1}^{n} f(c(i))\Delta_i x.$$

Again, by way of example, if $f(x) = x$, $P = \{0, \frac{1}{2}, 1\}$, and $c(1) = \frac{1}{4}$, $c(2) = \frac{3}{4}$, then

$$S(f; P, c) = \sum_{i=1}^{2} f(c(i))\Delta_i x$$

$$= f(\tfrac{1}{4}) \cdot \tfrac{1}{2} + f(\tfrac{3}{4}) \cdot \tfrac{1}{2}$$

$$= \tfrac{1}{2}(\tfrac{1}{4} + \tfrac{3}{4}) = \tfrac{1}{2}.$$

182 DEFINITION

Let f be defined and bounded over $[a, b]$. If there exists a real number l having the property that for every $\varepsilon > 0$ there exists a partition P_ε of $[a, b]$ such that

$$|S(f; P, c) - l| < \varepsilon$$

for all $P \supset P_\varepsilon$ and for all choice functions c associated with P, then

[1] f is said to be *Riemann integrable* over $[a, b]$, denoted by $f \in \mathcal{R}[a, b]$, and

[2] the number is called the *Riemann integral* of f over $[a, b]$, denoted either by

$$\int_a^b f(x)\,dx \qquad \text{or} \qquad \lim S(f; P, c).$$

If no such number l exists, then we shall say that

[1] f is not *Riemann integrable* over $[a, b]$, denoted by $f \notin \mathcal{R}[a, b]$, and that

[2] the Riemann integral of f over $[a, b]$ *does not exist* or $\lim S(f; P, c)$ *does not exist*.

Functions that are constant over an interval are integrable and have an easily computed integral.

183 THEOREM

If $f(x) = k$ for every $x \in [a, b]$, then $f \in \mathscr{R}[a, b]$ and

$$\int_a^b f(x)\, dx = k(b - a).$$

Proof

For every partition P of $[a, b]$ and every choice function c associated with P we have

$$S(f; P, c) = \sum_{i=1}^n f(c(i))\Delta_i x$$

$$= \sum_{i=1}^n k \cdot \Delta_i x = k \sum_{i=1}^n \Delta_i x$$

$$= k[(x_1 - x_0) + (x_2 - x_1) + \cdots + (x_n - x_{n-1})]$$

$$= k(x_n - x_0) = k(b - a).$$

Given $\varepsilon > 0$, let $P_\varepsilon = \{a, b\}$. If $P \supset P_\varepsilon$ and c is any choice function associated with P, then

$$|S(f; P, c) - k(b - a)| = 0 < \varepsilon.$$

Therefore $f \in \mathscr{R}[a, b]$, and

$$\int_a^b f(x)\, dx = k(b - a). \quad \square$$

EXERCISES

1 ▷ Prove that if $f \in \mathscr{R}[a, b]$, $k \in \mathbf{K}$, and $g(x) = f(x) - k$, then $g \in \mathscr{R}[a, b]$ and

$$\int_a^b g(x)\, dx = \int_a^b f(x)\, dx - k(b - a).$$

2 ▷ Prove that if $f_1 \in \mathscr{R}[a, b]$ and $f_2 \in \mathscr{R}[a, b]$, then $(f_1 + f_2) \in \mathscr{R}[a, b]$ and

$$\int_a^b (f_1 + f_2)(x)\, dx = \int_a^b f_1(x)\, dx + \int_a^b f_2(x)\, dx.$$

Use mathematical induction to extend this result to any finite sum of integrable functions.

3   Prove that if $f \in \mathcal{R}[a, b]$ and $k \in \mathbf{K}$, then $kf \in \mathcal{R}[a, b]$ and

$$\int_a^b kf(x)\,dx = k \int_a^b f(x)\,dx.$$

4   ▷ Prove that if P_1 and P_2 are partitions of an interval $[a, b]$, then $P_1 \cup P_2$ is also a partition of $[a, b]$.

5   ▷ Prove that if P_1 and P_2 are partitions of $[a, b]$ with $P_1 \supset P_2$, then $|P_1| \leq |P_2|$.

6   ▷ Prove that if $f \in \mathcal{R}[a, b]$ and $f(x) \geq 0$ for all $x \in [a, b]$, then

$$\int_a^b f(x)\,dx \geq 0.$$

7   Prove that if $f \in \mathcal{R}[a, b]$, $g \in \mathcal{R}[a, b]$, and $f(x) \leq g(x)$ for all $x \in [a, b]$, then

$$\int_a^b f(x)\,dx \leq \int_a^b g(x)\,dx.$$

Upper and Lower Integrals

Questions concerning the Riemann integrability of functions are often simplified by consideration of Darboux rather than Riemann sums. The reason for this is that the Darboux sums are not complicated by the presence of choice functions.

184 DEFINITION

Let f be defined and bounded over $[a, b]$, and let $P = \{x_0, \ldots, x_n\}$ be a partition of $[a, b]$. For each $i = 1, \ldots, n$ let

$$M_i = \text{lub}\{f(x) : x_{i-1} \leq x \leq x_i\}$$

and

$$m_i = \text{glb}\{f(x) : x_{i-1} \leq x \leq x_i\}.$$

The *upper Darboux sum* $D(f; p)$ is defined by

$$D(f; P) = \sum_{i=1}^n M_i \cdot \Delta_i x$$

and the *lower Darboux sum* $d(f; P)$ is defined by

$$d(f; P) = \sum_{i=1}^{n} m_i \cdot \Delta_i x.$$

The Darboux sums associated with a given partition hem in every Riemann sum associated with that partition.

185 THEOREM

Let f be defined and bounded over $[a, b]$, and let P be a partition of $[a, b]$. Then $d(f; P) \leq S(f; P, c) \leq D(f; P)$ for every choice function c associated with P.

Proof

If c is any choice function associated with P, then

$$x_{i-1} \leq c(i) \leq x_i \qquad \text{for every} \quad i = 1, \ldots, n.$$

Hence

$$m_i \leq f(c(i)) \leq M_i \qquad \text{for every} \quad i = 1, \ldots, n.$$

Since $\Delta_i x \, 0$,

$$m_i \Delta_i x \leq f(c(i)) \Delta_i x \leq M_i \Delta_i x \qquad \text{for every} \quad i = 1, \ldots, n.$$

Hence

$$d(f; P) \leq S(f; P, c) \leq D(f; P). \quad \square$$

Our next theorem describes how the Darboux sums behave with respect to partition refinement.

186 THEOREM

Let f be defined and bounded over $[a, b]$. If P_1 and P_2 are partitions of $[a, b]$ with $P_1 \supset P_2$, then

$$D(f; P_1) \leq D(f; P_2) \qquad \text{and} \qquad d(f; P_1) \geq d(f; P_2).$$

Proof

It suffices to show that the theorem holds when P_1 has exactly one more point than P_2. Let

$$P_2 = \{x_0, x_1, \ldots, x_j, x_{j+1}, \ldots, x_n\}$$

and

$$P_1 = \{x_0, x_1, \ldots, x_j, x^\bullet, x_{j+1}, \ldots, x_n\}.$$

Then

$$D(f; P_1) = M_1\Delta_1 x + \cdots + M_j\Delta_j x + \overline{M}_j\overline{\Delta}_j x + \overline{M}_{j+1}\overline{\Delta}_{j+1} x$$
$$+ M_{j+2}\Delta_{j+2} x + \cdots + M_n\Delta_n x$$

where

$$\overline{M}_j = \text{lub} \{ f(x) : x_j \le x \le x^\bullet),$$
$$\overline{M}_{j+1} = \text{lub} \{ f(x) : x^\bullet \le x \le x_{j+1} \},$$
$$\overline{\Delta}_j x = x^\bullet - x_j,$$

and

$$\overline{\Delta}_{j+1} x = x_{j+1} - x^\bullet.$$

Let $M_{j+1} = \text{lub}\{ f(x) : x_j \le x \le x_{j+1} \}$. Then $M_{j+1} \ge \overline{M}_j$ and $M_{j+1} \ge \overline{M}_{j+1}$, hence

$$D(f; P_1) \le M_1\Delta_1 x + \cdots + M_{j+1}\overline{\Delta}_j x + M_{j+1}\overline{\Delta}_{j+1} x$$
$$+ \cdots + M_n\Delta_n x$$
$$= M_1\Delta_1 x + \cdots + M_{j+1}(x^\bullet - x_j + x_{j+1} - x^\bullet)$$
$$+ \cdots + M_n\Delta_n x$$
$$= M_1\Delta_1 x + \cdots + M_{j+1}\Delta_{j+1} x + \cdots + M_n\Delta_n x$$
$$= D(f; P_2).$$

The proof that $d(f : P_1) \ge d(f; P_2)$ is left as an exercise for the reader. $\square$

187 THEOREM

Let $\mathscr{P}$ denote the set of all partitions of $[a, b]$. If f is defined and bounded over $[a, b]$, then the set

$$\{ D(f; P) : P \in \mathscr{P} \}$$

is bounded below, and the set

$$\{ d(f; P) : P \in \mathscr{P} \}$$

is bounded above.

Proof

Let $P_0 = \{ a, b \}$. If $P \in \mathscr{P}$ then $P \supset P_0$, so

$$d(f; P_0) \le d(f; P) \le D(f; P).$$

Hence $d(f; P_0)$ is a lower bound of

$$\{D(f; P) : P \in \mathscr{P}\}.$$

The proof that $D(f; P_0)$ is an upper bound of

$$\{d(f; P) : P \in \mathscr{P}\}$$

is left as an exercise. □

188 DEFINITION

Let $\mathscr{P}$ denote the set of all partitions of $[a, b]$, and let f be defined and bounded over $[a, b]$. The *upper Riemann integral* of f over $[a, b]$, denoted by $\overline{\int_a^b} f(x)\, dx$, is defined by

$$\overline{\int_a^b} f(x)\, dx = \mathrm{glb}\{D(f; P) : P \in \mathscr{P}\}.$$

The *lower Riemann integral* of f over $[a, b]$, denoted by $\underline{\int_a^b} f(x)\, dx$, is defined by

$$\underline{\int_a^b} f(x)\, dx = \mathrm{lub}\{d(f; P) : P \in \mathscr{P}\}.$$

189 THEOREM

If f is defined and bounded over $[a, b]$, then both $\overline{\int_a^b} f(x)\, dx$ and $\underline{\int_a^b} f(x)\, dx$ exist, and

$$\underline{\int_a^b} f(x)\, dx \le \overline{\int_a^b} f(x)\, dx.$$

Proof

The set $\{D(f; P) : P \in \mathscr{P}\}$ is bounded below and contains the number $D(f; \{a, b\})$. Hence $\overline{\int_a^b} f(x)\, dx$ exists. The set $\{d(f; P) : P \in \mathscr{P}\}$ is bounded above and contains the number $d(f; \{a, b\})$. Hence $\underline{\int_a^b} f(x)\, dx$ exists.

Now assume that $\overline{\int_a^b} f(x)\, dx < \underline{\int_a^b} f(x)\, dx$ for some function f. Then there exists $P_1 \in \mathscr{P}$ such that

$$d(f; P_1) > \overline{\int_a^b} f(x)\, dx.$$

Hence there exists $P_2 \in \mathscr{P}$ such that $D(f; P_2) < d(f; P_1)$. Let $P_3 = P_1 \cup P_2$. Then $P_3 \supset P_1$ and $P_3 \supset P_2$, so

$$D(f; P_3) \le D(f; P_2)$$

and

$$d(f; P_3) \ge d(f; P_1).$$

Therefore

$$D(f; P_3) < d(f; P_3).$$

This contradicts Theorem 185. Hence

$$\underline{\int_a^b} f(x)\, dx \le \overline{\int_a^b} f(x)\, dx$$

for every function f defined and bounded over $[a, b]$. □

EXERCISES

1 Complete the proof of Theorem 186.

2 Complete the proof of Theorem 187.

3 In the proof of Theorem 186, why does it suffice to consider only the case in which P_1 contains exactly one more point than P_2?

4 Let

$$f(x) = \begin{cases} 1 & \text{if } x \text{ is irrational} \\ 0 & \text{if } x \text{ is rational}. \end{cases}$$

Find $\overline{\int_0^1} f(x)\, dx$ and $\underline{\int_0^1} f(x)\, dx$.

5 ▷ Prove that if f is defined and bounded over $[a, b]$, $k \in \mathbf{K}$, and

$$g(x) = f(x) - k,$$

then

$$D(g; P) = D(f; P) - k(b - a)$$

for every partition P of $[a, b]$.

Necessary and Sufficient Conditions for Integrability

The upper and lower Darboux sums, and through them the upper and lower integrals, provide relatively simple and extremely useful tests for integrability.

190 THEOREM

Let f be defined and bounded over $[a, b]$. Then $f \in \mathcal{R}[a, b]$ if and only if

$$\overline{\int_a^b} f(x)\, dx = \underline{\int_a^b} f(x)\, dx.$$

If $f \in \mathcal{R}[a, b]$, then

$$\int_a^b f(x)\, dx = \overline{\int_a^b} f(x)\, dx = \underline{\int_a^b} f(x)\, dx.$$

Proof

Assume that $f \in \mathcal{R}[a, b]$. We wish to show that

$$\int_a^b f(x)\, dx = \overline{\int_a^b} f(x)\, dx = \underline{\int_a^b} f(x)\, dx.$$

Let $l = \int_a^b f(x)\, dx$. Assume that $D(f; P_0) < l$ for some $P_0 \in \mathcal{P}$ ($\mathcal{P}$ denotes, as usual, the set of all partitions of $[a, b]$). Then

$$l - D(f; P_0) > 0.$$

Let $\varepsilon = l - D(f; P_0)$. Then there exists $P_\varepsilon \in \mathcal{P}$ such that

$$|S(f; P, c) - l| < \varepsilon$$

for all $P \supset P_\varepsilon$ and for all choice functions c associated with P. Let

$$P_2 = P_\varepsilon \cup P_0.$$

Then $P_2 \supset P_\varepsilon$, so

$$|S(f; P_2, c) - l| < \varepsilon$$

for all choice functions c associated with P_2. Hence

$$l - \varepsilon < S(f; P_2, c) < l + \varepsilon \qquad \text{for all} \quad c,$$

so that

$$l - (l - D(f; P_0)) < S(f; P_2, c) \qquad \text{for all} \quad c,$$

and finally

$$D(f; P_0) < S(f; P_2, c)$$

for all choice functions c associated with P_2. But $P_2 \supset P_0$, so

$$D(f; P_2) \leq D(f; P_0).$$

Therefore

$$D(f ; P_2) < S(f ; P_2, c)$$

for all choice functions c associated with P_2. This contradicts Theorem 185. Hence

$$D(f ; P) \geq l \qquad \text{for every} \quad P \in \mathscr{P}.$$

It can also be shown that

$$d(f ; P) \leq l \qquad \text{for every} \quad P \in \mathscr{P}.$$

The details of the proof are left as an exercise.

Given $\varepsilon > 0$, we now wish to find a particular partition P of $[a, b]$ such that

$$D(f ; P) < l + \varepsilon.$$

First, there exists $P_{\varepsilon/2} \in \mathscr{P}$ such that

$$|S(f ; P, c) - l| < \frac{\varepsilon}{2}$$

for all $P \supset P_{\varepsilon/2}$ and for all choice functions c associated with P. Let

$$P_{\varepsilon/2} = \{x_0, \ldots, x_n\}.$$

Then for each $i = 1, \ldots, n$ there exists $x_i^\bullet$ in $[x_{i-1}, x_i]$ such that

$$f(x_i^\bullet) > M_i - \frac{\varepsilon}{2(b - a)},$$

where

$$M_i = \text{lub}\{f(x) : x_{i-1} \leq x \leq x_i\}.$$

Let

$$c_0(i) = x_i^\bullet, \qquad i = 1, \ldots, n.$$

Then

$$S(f ; P_{\varepsilon/2}, c_0) = \sum_{i=1}^{n} f(c_0(i))\Delta_i x$$

$$> \sum_{i=1}^{n} \left(M_i - \frac{\varepsilon}{2(b - a)} \right)\Delta_i x$$

$$= \sum_{i=1}^{n} M_i \Delta_i x - \frac{\varepsilon}{2(b - a)} \sum_{i=1}^{n} \Delta_i x$$

$$= D(f ; P_{\varepsilon/2}) - \frac{\varepsilon}{2}.$$

Now $P_{\varepsilon/2} \supset P_{\varepsilon/2}$, so

$$|S(f; P_{\varepsilon/2}, c_0) - l| < \frac{\varepsilon}{2},$$

whence

$$l - \frac{\varepsilon}{2} < S(f; P_{\varepsilon/2}, c_0) < l + \frac{\varepsilon}{2}.$$

Since $D(f; P_{\varepsilon/2}) - \varepsilon/2 < S(f; P_{\varepsilon/2}, c_0)$, we have

$$D(f; P_{\varepsilon/2}) - \frac{\varepsilon}{2} < l + \frac{\varepsilon}{2}.$$

Therefore $D(f; P_{\varepsilon/2}) < l + \varepsilon$.

It now follows that

$$l = \text{glb}\,\{D(f; P) : P \in \mathscr{P}\}.$$

Therefore

$$\int_a^b f(x)\,dx = \overline{\int_a^b} f(x)\,dx.$$

In an analogous manner (the details of which should be supplied by the reader) it can be shown that given $\varepsilon > 0$ there exists a partition P of $[a, b]$ such that

$$d(f; P) > l - \varepsilon.$$

It then follows that

$$\int_a^b f(x)\,dx = \underline{\int_a^b} f(x)\,dx.$$

Conversely, assume that

$$\overline{\int_a^b} f(x)\,dx = \underline{\int_a^b} f(x)\,dx.$$

Let

$$l = \overline{\int_a^b} f(x)\,dx \;\left(= \underline{\int_a^b} f(x)\,dx.\right)$$

Given $\varepsilon > 0$, there exists $P_1 \in \mathscr{P}$ such that

$$D(f; P_1) < l + \varepsilon,$$

and there exists $P_2 \in \mathscr{P}$ such that $d(f; P_2) > l - \varepsilon$. Let $P_\varepsilon = P_1 \cup P_2$. If $P \supset P_\varepsilon$, then $P \supset \mathscr{P}_1$ and $P \supset P_2$, so

$$l - \varepsilon < d(f; P_2) \leq d(f; P) \leq S(f; P, c) \leq D(f; P) \leq D(f; P_1) < l + \varepsilon$$

for every choice function c associated with P. Hence, if $P \supset P_\varepsilon$, then

$$l - \varepsilon < s(f; P, c) < l + \varepsilon,$$

and so

$$|S(f; P, c) - l| < \varepsilon$$

for every choice function c associated with P. Therefore $f \in \mathscr{R}[a, b]$. $\square$

Be careful not to miss the full import of our next theorem. It is necessary and sufficient that the stated inequality hold for only one particular partition of $[a, b]$.

191 THEOREM

Let f be defined and bounded over $[a, b]$. Then $f \in \mathscr{R}[a, b]$ if and only if for every $\varepsilon > 0$ there exists a partition P_ε of $[a, b]$ such that

$$D(f; P_\varepsilon) - d(f; P_\varepsilon) < \varepsilon.$$

Proof

Assume that $f \in \mathscr{R}[a, b]$. Then

$$\overline{\int_a^b} f(x) \, dx = \underline{\int_a^b} f(x) \, dx = l.$$

Given $\varepsilon > 0$ there exists $P_1 \in \mathscr{P}$ such that $D(f; P_1) < l + \varepsilon/2$, and there exists $P_2 \in \mathscr{P}$ such that $d(f; P_2) > l - \varepsilon/2$. Let $P_\varepsilon = P_1 \cup P_2$. Then $P_\varepsilon \supset P_1$ and $P_\varepsilon \supset P_2$, so

$$D(f; P_\varepsilon) \leq D(f; P_1) < l + \frac{\varepsilon}{2},$$

and

$$d(f; P_\varepsilon) \geq d(f; P_2) > l - \frac{\varepsilon}{2}.$$

Therefore

$$D(f; P_\varepsilon) - d(f; P_\varepsilon) < \varepsilon.$$

Conversely, assume that for every $\varepsilon > 0$ there exists $P_\varepsilon \in \mathscr{P}$ such that

$$D(f; P_\varepsilon) - d(f; P_\varepsilon) < \varepsilon.$$

Let

$$l = \overline{\int_a^b} f(x)\,dx.$$

Then

$$d(f; P) \le \underline{\int_a^b} f(x)\,dx \le \overline{\int_a^b} f(x)\,dx = l$$

for every $P \in \mathscr{P}$. Hence l is an upper bound of

$$\{d(f; P) : P \in \mathscr{P}\}.$$

Given $\varepsilon > 0$ there exists P_ε such that

$$D(f; P_\varepsilon) - d(f; P_\varepsilon) < \varepsilon.$$

Now $D(f; P_\varepsilon) \ge l$, so

$$l - d(f; P_\varepsilon) \le D(f; P_\varepsilon) - d(f; P_\varepsilon) < \varepsilon,$$

and so

$$d(f; P_\varepsilon) > l - \varepsilon.$$

Therefore

$$l = \mathrm{lub}\{d(f; P) : P \in \mathscr{P}\} = \underline{\int_a^b} f(x)\,dx.$$

It then follows that

$$\underline{\int_a^b} f(x)\,dx = \overline{\int_a^b} f(x)\,dx,$$

and so

$$f \in \mathscr{R}[a, b]. \quad \square$$

As an application of Theorem 191 we shall show that every continuous function is Riemann integrable. First, however, we need to establish the following property of functions that are continuous over a closed interval.

192 THEOREM   Uniform Continuity

If f is continuous over $[a, b]$, then for every $\varepsilon > 0$ there exists $\delta > 0$ such that

$$|f(x_1) - f(x_2)| < \varepsilon$$

for all x_1 and x_2 in $[a, b]$ with

$$|x_1 - x_2| < \delta.$$

(That is, f is *uniformly continuous* over $[a, b]$.)

Proof

Let $\varepsilon > 0$ be given. Since f is continuous at each $p \in [a, b]$, for each such p there exists $\delta_p > 0$ such that

$$|f(x) - f(p)| < \frac{\varepsilon}{2}$$

for all $x \in [a, b]$ with $|x - p| < \delta_p$.

Let

$$\mathcal{C} = \{]p - \tfrac{1}{2}\delta_p, p + \tfrac{1}{2}\delta_p[: p \in [a, b]\}.$$

Then $\mathcal{C}$ is an open covering of $[a, b]$. Since $[a, b]$ is compact, there are a finite number of points $p_1, \ldots, p_n$ in $[a, b]$ such that

$$\{]p_i - \tfrac{1}{2}\delta_{p_i}, p_i + \tfrac{1}{2}\delta_{p_i}[: i = 1, \ldots, n\}$$

covers $[a, b]$.

Let

$$\delta = \min\{\tfrac{1}{2}\delta_{p_1}, \ldots, \tfrac{1}{2}\delta_{p_n}\}.$$

Suppose $x_1, x_2 \in [a, b]$ and $|x_1 - x_2| < \delta$. Then there exists an integer i, $1 \le i \le n$, such that

$$x_1 \in]p_i - \tfrac{1}{2}\delta_{p_i}, p_i + \tfrac{1}{2}\delta_{p_i}[.$$

Now

$$|x_2 - p_i| = |(x_2 - x_1) + (x_1 - p_i)|$$

$$\le |x_2 - x_1| + |x_1 - p_i|$$

$$< \delta + \tfrac{1}{2}\delta_{p_i} \le \tfrac{1}{2}\delta_{p_i} + \tfrac{1}{2}\delta_{p_i}$$

$$= \delta_{p_i}.$$

Hence

$$|x_2 - p_i| < \delta_{p_i}$$

and

$$|x_1 - p_i| < \tfrac{1}{2}\delta_{p_i} < \delta_{p_i}.$$

Therefore

$$|f(x_1) - f(x_2)| = |(f(x_1) - f(p_i)) + (f(p_i) - f(x_2))|$$
$$\leq |f(x_1) - f(p_i)| + |f(x_2) - f(p_i)|$$
$$< \frac{\varepsilon}{2} + \frac{\varepsilon}{2} = \varepsilon. \quad \square$$

193 THEOREM

If f is continuous over $[a, b]$, then $f \in \mathcal{R}[a, b]$.

Proof

Let $\varepsilon > 0$ be given. It follows from Theorem 192 that there exists $\delta > 0$ such that

$$|f(x_1) - f(x_2)| < \frac{\varepsilon}{b - a}$$

for all $x_1, x_2 \in [a, b]$ with $|x_1 - x_2| < \delta$.

Now $\delta > 0$ and $(b - a) > 0$. Hence (Archimedean order) there exists a positive integer n such that

$$n\delta > b - a.$$

Thus

$$\frac{b - a}{n} < \delta.$$

Let

$$x_0 = a, x_1 = a + \frac{b - a}{n}, x_2 = a + \frac{2(b - a)}{n}, \ldots, x_n = a + \frac{n(b - a)}{n} = b,$$

and let

$$P_\varepsilon = \{x_0, x_1, \ldots, x_n\}.$$

Then P_ε is a partition of $[a, b]$, and

$$\Delta_i x = \frac{b - a}{n}, \qquad i = 1, \ldots, n.$$

Since f is continuous over each subinterval $[x_{i-1}, x_i]$, there exist $x_i^\bullet$ and $x_i^{\bullet\bullet}$ in $[x_{i-1}, x_i]$ $(i = 1, \ldots, n)$ such that

$$f(x_i^\bullet) = m_i \quad (= \text{glb}\{f(x) : x_{i-1} \leq x \leq x_i\})$$

and

$$f(x_i^{\bullet\bullet}) = M_i \quad (= \text{lub}\{f(x) : x_{i-1} \leq x \leq x_i\}).$$

Now

$$|x_i^{\bullet\bullet} - x_i^{\bullet}| \le x_i - x_{i-1} = \Delta_i x = \frac{b-a}{n} < \delta,$$

$i = 1, \ldots, n$. Therefore

$$M_i - m_i = f(x_i^{\bullet\bullet}) - f(x_i^{\bullet})$$

$$= |f(x_i^{\bullet\bullet}) - f(x_i^{\bullet})| < \frac{\varepsilon}{b-a}.$$

It follows that

$$D(f; P_\varepsilon) - d(f; P_\varepsilon) = \sum_{i=1}^{n} M_i \Delta_i x - \sum_{i=1}^{n} m_i \Delta_i x$$

$$= \sum_{i=1}^{n} (M_i - m_i) \Delta_i x < \frac{\varepsilon}{b-a} \sum_{i=1}^{n} \Delta_i x = \varepsilon.$$

Therefore $f \in \mathcal{R}[a, b]$. $\square$

EXERCISES

1   Let

$$f(x) = \begin{cases} x & \text{if } x \text{ is irrational,} \\ x^2 & \text{if } x \text{ is rational.} \end{cases}$$

Show that

$$\overline{\int_0^1} f(x)\,dx = \int_0^1 x\,dx,$$

and that

$$\underline{\int_0^1} f(x)\,dx = \int_0^1 x^2\,dx.$$

2   Let a, b, and c be real numbers with $a < b < c$, and let f be defined and bounded over $[a, c]$. Prove that if $f \in \mathcal{R}[a, b]$ and $f \in \mathcal{R}[b, c]$, then $f \in \mathcal{R}[a, c]$ and

$$\int_a^c f(x)\,dx = \int_a^b f(x)\,dx + \int_b^c f(x)\,dx.$$

3   Complete the details of the proof of Theorem 190.

4   Assume that $f \in \mathcal{R}[a, b]$. Prove that if g is defined and bounded

over $[a, b]$, and if $f(x) = g(x)$ for all but a finite number of x in $[a, b]$, then $g \in \mathscr{R}[a, b]$ and

$$\int_a^b g(x)\,dx = \int_a^b f(x)\,dx.$$

5   Prove that if $f \in \mathscr{R}[a, b]$, then $|f| \in \mathscr{R}[a, b]$, and

$$\left| \int_a^b f(x)\,dx \right| \le \int_a^b |f|(x)\,dx.$$

[Note : $|f|$ is the function defined by $|f|(x) = |f(x)|$.]

Mean Value Theorem for Integrals

Our work in integration theory up to this point has been concerned chiefly with the existence of the Riemann integral. We shall now begin to turn our attention to the matter of evaluation of the integral. It is manifestly clear that evaluation by means of direct application of Definition 182 is impractical, since that definition offers little information as to how the magic number l is determined. Our first theorem provides at least a ball-park estimate of l.

194 THEOREM

Let f be defined and bounded over $[a, b]$, and let

$$M = \operatorname{lub}\{f(x) : x \in [a, b]\},$$

$$m = \operatorname{glb}\{f(x) : x \in [a, b]\}.$$

Then

$$m(b - a) \le \underline{\int_a^b} f(x)\,dx \le \overline{\int_a^b} f(x)\,dx \le M(b - a).$$

In particular, if $f \in \mathscr{R}[a, b]$, then

$$m(b - a) \le \int_a^b f(x)\,dx \le M(b - a).$$

Proof

Let $P_0 = \{a, b\}$. Then

$$D(f; P_0) = M(b - a),$$

and so

$$M(b - a) \geq \overline{\int_a^b} f(x)\, dx.$$

Also

$$d(f; P_0) = m(b - a),$$

and so

$$m(b - a) \leq \underline{\int_a^b} f(x)\, dx.$$

That $\underline{\int_a^b} f(x)\, dx \leq \overline{\int_a^b} f(x)\, dx$ follows from Theorem 189, and the last sentence of the theorem follows from Theorem 190. $\square$

The intermediate value theorem for continuous functions can be combined with Theorem 194 to yield the following.

195 THEOREM   Mean Value Theorem for Integrals

If f is continuous over $[a, b]$, then there exists $x_0 \in [a, b]$ such that $\int_a^b f(x)\, dx = f(x_0) \cdot (b - a)$.

Proof

It follows from Theorem 193 that $f \in \mathscr{R}[a, b]$. Let

$$k = \frac{1}{b - a} \int_a^b f(x)\, dx.$$

Then $\int_a^b f(x)\, dx = k(b - a)$. Furthermore, it follows from Theorem 194 that

$$m \leq k \leq M,$$

where m and M are defined as in Theorem 194. Now f is continuous over $[a, b]$, so there exists $x_1 \in [a, b]$ such that $f(x_1) = m$ and there exists $x_2 \in [a, b]$ such that $f(x_2) = M$. Since $f(x_1) \leq k \leq f(x_2)$ it follows from the intermediate value theorem that there exists $x_0 \in [a, b]$ such that $f(x_0) = k$. Therefore

$$\int_a^b f(x)\, dx = f(x_0) \cdot (b - a). \quad \square$$

EXERCISES

1   Prove that

$$-3 \le \int_0^3 (x^2 - 2x)\,dx \le 9.$$

2   ▷ Let M be a nonempty, bounded subset of **K**, and let

$$-M = \{-x : x \in M\}.$$

Prove that

$$\mathrm{glb}(-M) = -\mathrm{lub}\,M$$

and that

$$\mathrm{lub}(-M) = -\mathrm{glb}\,M$$

3   Give a geometric interpretation of the mean value theorem for integrals in the case that $f(x) \ge 0$ for all $x \in [a, b]$.

Convergence in Norm

For many theoretical considerations, and for many practical applications as well, it is desirable to be able to identify the Riemann integral as the limit of the Riemann sums in a manner which differs from that stated in Definition 182. The type of limit described in Definition 182 can be thought of as a "partition refinement" limit. It is possible, of course, to successively refine a partition without having the partition norm tend to zero. Nevertheless, the partition refinement limit of the Riemann sums is equivalent to their limit in norm, which we now define.

196 DEFINITION

Let f be defined and bounded over $[a, b]$. We shall say that the Riemann sum $S(f; P, c)$ *converges in norm* iff there is a real number l with the property that for every $\varepsilon > 0$ there exists $\delta > 0$ such that

$$|S(f; P, c) - l| < \varepsilon$$

for all partitions P with $|P| < \delta$ and for all choice functions c associated with P. Notation:

$$\lim_{|P| \to 0} S(f; P, c) = l.$$

197 THEOREM

Let f be defined and bounded over $[a, b]$. Then $f \in \mathscr{R}[a, b]$ if and only if $S(f; P, c)$ converges in norm. Moreover, if $f \in \mathscr{R}[a, b]$, then

$$\int_a^b f(x)\,dx = \lim_{|P| \to 0} S(f; P, c).$$

Proof

Assume that $S(f; P, c)$ converges in norm. Then there exists $l \in \mathbf{K}$ such that

$$\lim_{|P| \to 0} S(f; P, c) = l.$$

Given $\varepsilon > 0$ there exists $\delta > 0$ such that

$$|S(f; P, c) - l| < \varepsilon$$

for all P with $|P| < \delta$ and for all c associated with P. Choose a positive integer n so that

$$n\delta > b - a$$

(Archimedean order), and let

$$x_0 = a, \ x_1 = a + \frac{1}{n}(b - a), \dots, x_n = a + \frac{n}{n}(b - a) = b.$$

Let

$$P_\varepsilon = \{x_0, x_1, \dots, x_n\}.$$

Then

$$\Delta_i x = \frac{b - a}{n} < \delta \qquad \text{for} \quad i = 1, \dots, n,$$

so $|P_\varepsilon| < \delta$. If $P \supset P_\varepsilon$, then $|P| \leq |P_\varepsilon| < \delta$, so $|S(f; P, c) - l| < \varepsilon$ for all c associated with P. Hence $f \in \mathscr{R}[a, b]$, and

$$\int_a^b f(x)\,dx = l = \lim_{|P| \to 0} S(f; P, c).$$

Conversely, assume that $f \in \mathscr{R}[a, b]$, and let $l = \int_a^b f(x)\,dx$. We must show that $\lim_{|P| \to 0} S(f; P, c) = l$.

[1] We begin by showing that for every $\varepsilon > 0$ there exists $\delta > 0$ such that $D(f; P) < \int_a^b f(x)\,dx + \varepsilon$ for all P with $|P| < \delta$:

Assume that $f(x) \geq 0$ for all $x \in [a, b]$. Given $\varepsilon > 0$ there exists a partition $P_0 = \{x_0, \ldots, x_n\}$ of $[a, b]$ such that

$$D(f; P_0) < \overline{\int_a^b} f(x)\, dx + \frac{\varepsilon}{2}.$$

Let

$$M = \text{lub}\{f(x) : x \in [a, b]\}.$$

If $M = 0$, then $f(x) = 0$ for all $x \in [a, b]$, and so $\overline{\int_a^b} f(x)\, dx = 0$; hence

$$D(f; P) = 0 < \overline{\int_a^b} f(x)\, dx + \varepsilon$$

for every partition P. If $M \neq 0$, let

$$\delta = \min\left\{ \Delta_1 x, \ldots, \Delta_n x, \frac{\varepsilon}{2Mn} \right\}.$$

If $P = \{x_0', \ldots, x_m'\}$ is any partition of $[a, b]$ with $|P| < \delta$, then

$$
\begin{aligned}
D(f; P) &= \sum_{i=1}^m M_i' \Delta_i x' \\
&= \sum \{M_i' \Delta_i x' : [x_{i-1}', x_i'] \subset [x_{j-1}, x_j] \\
&\quad \text{for some } j = 1, \ldots, n\} \\
&\quad + \sum \{M_i' \Delta_i x' : x_j \in \,]x_{i-1}', x_i'[\\
&\quad \text{for some } j = 1, \ldots, n\} \\
&= D_1(f; P) + D_2(f; P).
\end{aligned}
$$

Now

$$D_1(f; P) \leq D(f; P \cup P_0) \leq D(f; P_0) \leq \overline{\int_a^b} f(x)\, dx + \frac{\varepsilon}{2}.$$

Also

$$D_2(f; P) \leq Mn|P| < Mn\delta \leq \frac{\varepsilon}{2}.$$

Therefore

$$D(f; P) < \left(\overline{\int_a^b} f(x)\, dx + \frac{\varepsilon}{2} \right) + \frac{\varepsilon}{2} = \overline{\int_a^b} f(x)\, dx + \varepsilon$$

for all P with $|P| < \delta$.

Now if f is any function defined and bounded over $[a, b]$, let

$$m = \text{glb}\{f(x) : x \in [a, b]\}.$$

Then $f(x) \geq m$ for all $x \in [a, b]$, and so the function g defined by $g(x) = f(x) - m$ has the property that $g(x) \geq 0$ for all $x \in [a, b]$. Furthermore (see Exercise 5, p.135),

$$D(g; P) = D(f; P) - m(b - a).$$

If $l^{\bullet} = \int_a^b g(x)\,dx$, then it follows from the previous argument that for every $\varepsilon > 0$ there exists $\delta > 0$ such that

$$D(g; P) < l^{\bullet} + \varepsilon$$

for all P with $|P| < \delta$. Therefore

$$D(f; P) - m(b - a) < l^{\bullet} + \varepsilon,$$

whence

$$D(f; P) < (l^{\bullet} + m(b - a)) + \varepsilon$$

for all P with $|P| < \delta$. Now $f \in \mathscr{R}[a, b]$, and so (see Exercise 1, p.130)

$$l^{\bullet} = \int_a^{\overline{b}} g(x)\,dx = \int_a^b g(x)\,dx$$

$$= \int_a^b f(x)\,dx - m(b - a) = \int_a^{\overline{b}} f(x)\,dx - m(b - a).$$

Hence

$$d(f; P) < \int_a^b f(x)\,dx + \varepsilon$$

for all P with $|P| < \delta$.

[2] Now we shall show that for every $\varepsilon > 0$ there exists $\delta > 0$ such that

$$d(f; P) > \int_a^b f(x)\,dx - \varepsilon$$

for all partitions P with $|P| < \delta$:

Now

$$d(f; P) = \sum_{i-1}^n m_i \Delta_i x = - \sum_{i=1}^n (-m_i)\Delta_i x.$$

Also

$$-m_i = \text{glb}\{f(x) : x_{i-1} \leq x_1 \leq x_i\}$$

$$= \text{lub}\{-f(x) : x_{i-1} \leq x_i \leq x_i\}$$

(Exercise 2, p. 146), so that

$$d(f; P) = -D(-f; P).$$

By part [1], given $\varepsilon > 0$ there exists $\delta > 0$ such that

$$D(-f; P) < \int_a^{\overline{b}} (-f(x))\, dx + \varepsilon$$

for all P with $|P| < \delta$. But

$$\int_a^{\overline{b}} (-f(x))\, dx = \text{glb} \{D(-f; P) : P \in \mathscr{P}\}$$

$$= \text{glb} \{-d(f; P) : P \in \mathscr{P}\}$$

$$= -\text{lub} \{d(f; P) : P \in \mathscr{P}\}$$

$$= -\int_{\underline{a}}^b f(x)\, dx.$$

Therefore

$$-d(f; P) < -\int_{\underline{a}}^b f(x)\, dx + \varepsilon$$

for all P with $|P| < \delta$, and so

$$d(f; P) > \int_{\underline{a}}^b f(x)\, dx - \varepsilon$$

for all P with $|P| < \delta$.

We now return to the crux of the proof. Since $f \in \mathscr{R}[a, b]$,

$$\int_{\underline{a}}^b f(x)\, dx = \int_a^{\overline{b}} f(x)\, dx = \int_a^b f(x)\, dx = l.$$

Given $\varepsilon > 0$, choose δ_1 so that

$$D(f; P) < l + \varepsilon$$

for all P with $|P| < \delta_1$, and choose δ_2 so that

$$d(f; P) > l - \varepsilon$$

for all P with $|P| < \delta_2$. Let $\delta = \min \{\delta_1, \delta_2\}$. If P is any partition of $[a, b]$ with $|P| < \delta$, then

$$l - \varepsilon < d(f, P) \leq S(f; P, c) \leq D(f; P) < l + \varepsilon$$

for every c associated with P, so

$$|S(f; P, c) - l| < \varepsilon$$

for all c. Therefore $\lim_{|P| \to 0} S(f; P, c) = l$. $\square$

Our next theorem tells us that if a function is integrable over a certain closed interval, then it is also integrable over every closed subinterval of that interval.

198 THEOREM

Let f be defined and bounded over $[a, b]$. If $f \in \mathcal{R}[a, b]$, then $f \in \mathcal{R}[c, d]$ for every pair of numbers c and d with $a \leq c < d \leq b$.

Proof

Assume that f is not integrable over $[c, d]$. Then, by Theorem 191, there exists $\varepsilon_0 > 0$ such that

$$D(f; P) - d(f; P) \geq \varepsilon_0$$

for every partition P of $[c, d]$.

Since $f \in \mathcal{R}[a, b]$, there is a partition P_0 of $[a, b]$ such that

$$D(f; P_0) - d(f; P_0) < \varepsilon_0.$$

Let $P^{\bullet} = P_0 \cup \{c, d\}$. Then $P^{\bullet}$ is a partition of $[a, b]$ and $P^{\bullet} \supset P_0$. We then have

$$D(f; P^{\bullet}) \leq D(f; P_0)$$

and

$$d(f; P^{\bullet}) \geq d(f; P_0),$$

so

$$D(f; P^{\bullet}) - d(f; P^{\bullet}) \leq D(f; P_0) - d(f; P_0) < \varepsilon_0.$$

Now $c \in P^{\bullet}$ and $d \in P^{\bullet}$. Hence

$$P^{\bullet} \cap [a, c] \text{ is a partition of } [a, c],$$

$$P^{\bullet} \cap [c, d] \text{ is a partition of } [c, d],$$

and

$$P^{\bullet} \cap [d, b] \text{ is a partition of } [d, b],$$

and

$$(P^{\bullet} \cap [a, c]) \cup (P^{\bullet} \cap [c, d]) \cup (P^{\bullet} \cap [d, b])$$

$$= P^{\bullet} \cap ([a, c] \cup [c, d] \cup [d, b])$$

$$= P^{\bullet} \cap [a, b] = P^{\bullet}.$$

Hence

$$D(f; P^\bullet) = D(f; P^\bullet \cap [a, c]) + D(f; P^\bullet \cap [c, d]) + D(f; P^\bullet \cap [d, b])$$
$$= S_1 + S_2 + S_3.$$

Similarly

$$d(f; P^\bullet) = d(f; P^\bullet \cap [a, c]) + d(f; P^\bullet \cap [c, d]) + d(f; P^\bullet \cap [d, b])$$
$$= s_1 + s_2 + s_3.$$

Therefore

$$D(f; P^\bullet) - d(f; P^\bullet) = (S_1 - s_1) + (S_2 - s_2) + (S_3 - s_3) < \varepsilon_0,$$

and so

$$S_2 - s_2 < \varepsilon_0 - (S_1 - s_1) - (S_3 - s_3) < \varepsilon_0.$$

Hence

$$D(f; P^\bullet \cap [c, d]) - d(f; P^\bullet \cap [c, d]) < \varepsilon_0,$$

contradicting the choice of ε_0. Therefore $f \in \mathcal{R}[c, d]$. $\square$

EXERCISES

1   Let f be defined and bounded over $[a, c]$. Prove that if $f \in \mathcal{R}[a, c]$ and $a < b < c$, then

$$\int_a^c f(x)\, dx = \int_a^b f(x)\, dx + \int_b^c f(x)\, dx.$$

2   Let f be defined and bounded over $[a, b]$, and let P be a sequence of partitions of $[a, b]$ having the property that $\lim |P_n| = 0$. For notational convenience, assume

$$P_n = \{x_0, \ldots, x_n\}.$$

Prove that if $f \in \mathcal{R}[a, b]$, then

$$\int_a^b f(x)\, dx = \lim \left(\sum_{i=1}^n f(x_i)\Delta_i x \right) = \lim \left(\sum_{i=1}^n f(x_{i-1})\Delta_i x \right).$$

3   Give an example of a function f that is defined and bounded over $[a, b]$ and which has both of the following properties:

(a) There exists a sequence P of partitions of $[a, b]$ with $P_n = \{x_0, \ldots, x_n\}$ and $\lim |P_n| = 0$ such that

$$\lim \left(\sum_{i=1}^n f(x_i)\Delta_i x \right) = \lim \left(\sum_{i=1}^n f(x_{i-1})\Delta_i x \right) = 0.$$

(b) $f \notin \mathcal{R}[0, 1]$.

In Exercises 4 and 5, refer to Definition 199 for the meaning of $\int_x^{x+h} f(t)\,dt$ in case $h < 0$.

4 ▷ Let f be defined and bounded over $[a, b]$. Prove that if $f \in \mathcal{R}[a, b]$, $x \in \,]a, b[$, and $|h|$ is sufficiently small (but positive), then

$$\int_a^{x+h} f(t)\,dt - \int_a^x f(t)\,dt = \int_x^{x+h} f(t)\,dt.$$

5 ▷ Let f be defined and continuous over $[a, b]$. Prove that if $x \in \,]a, b[$, and $|h|$ is sufficiently small (but positive), then there exists $x_0 \in [a, b]$ with $|x - x_0| \le |h|$ such that

$$\int_x^{x+h} f(t)\,dt = f(x_0) \cdot h.$$

6   Let f be continuous over $[a, b]$, and assume that $f(x) \ge 0$ for every $x \in [a, b]$. Prove that if $\int_a^b f(x)\,dx = 0$, then $f(x) = 0$ for every $x \in [a, b]$.

7   Let f be defined and bounded over $[a, b]$. Prove that if there exists a real number l such that

$$\lim S(f; P_n, c_n) = l$$

for every sequence of partitions P with $\lim |P_n| = 0$ and for every sequence c of choice functions such that c_n is associated with P_n, then $f \in \mathcal{R}[a, b]$ and

$$\int_a^b f(x)\,dx = l.$$

The Fundamental Theorem of Integral Calculus

We are finally in a position to apply the ball-park estimate of an integral provided by the mean value theorem to the problem of exact evaluation. First we extend the definition of the integral.

199 DEFINITION

Let $f \in \mathcal{R}[a, b]$. We define $\int_b^a f(x)\,dx$ by

$$\int_b^a f(x)\,dx = -\int_a^b f(x)\,dx.$$

Furthermore, for each $c \in [a, b]$ we define

$$\int_c^c f(x)\, dx = 0.$$

200 THEOREM

Let f be continuous over $[a, b]$, and for each $x \in [a, b]$ let

$$F(x) = \int_a^x f(t)\, dt.$$

Then F is continuous over $[a, b]$, differentiable over $]a, b[$, and

$$F'(x) = f(x) \qquad \text{for every} \quad x \in\,]a, b[\,.$$

Proof

Let $x \in\,]a, b[$. Then

$$F'(x) = \lim_{h \to 0} \frac{F(x + h) - F(x)}{h},$$

$$= \lim_{h \to 0} \frac{\int_a^{x+h} f(t)\, dt - \int_a^x f(t)\, dt}{h},$$

$$= \lim_{h \to 0} \frac{\int_x^{x+h} f(t)\, dt}{h} \qquad \text{(Exercise 4, p. 153)}$$

$$= \lim_{h \to 0} \frac{f(x_0) \cdot h}{h}, \qquad |x - x_0| \le |h| \text{ (Exercise 5, p. 153)}$$

$$= \lim_{h \to 0} f(x_0) = f(x) \qquad \text{(since } f \text{ is continuous).}$$

Hence F is differentiable over $]a, b[$, and $F'(x) = f(x)$ for every $x \in\,]a, b[$.

Since F is differentiable at each point of $]a, b[$, F is continuous over $]a, b[$. To prove that F is continuous over $[a, b]$ it then suffices to show that

$$\lim_{x \to a^+} F(x) = F(a),$$

and that

$$\lim_{x \to b^-} F(x) = F(b).$$

If $a < x \le b$, then

$$F(x) = \int_a^x f(t)\, dt = f(x_0) \cdot (x - a), \qquad a \le x_0 \le x,$$

so

$$\lim_{x \to a^+} F(x) = \lim_{x \to a} f(x_0) \cdot (x - a), \qquad a \leq x_0 \leq x,$$

$$= f(a) \cdot 0,$$

$$= 0,$$

$$= F(a).$$

Similarly, if $a \leq x \leq b$, then

$$F(b) - F(x) = \int_x^b f(t) \, dt$$

$$= f(x_1)(b - x), \qquad x \leq x_1 \leq b,$$

so

$$\lim_{x \to b^-} (F(b) - F(x)) = \lim_{x \to b^-} f(x_1) \cdot (b - x) = f(b) \cdot 0 = 0.$$

Therefore

$$\lim_{x \to b^-} F(x) = F(b). \quad \square$$

201 THEOREM   Fundamental Theorem of Integral Calculus

Let f be continuous over $[a, b]$. If G is continuous over $[a, b]$ and $G'(x) = f(x)$ for all $x \in \,]a, b[$, then

$$\int_a^b f(t) \, dt = G(b) - G(a).$$

Proof

Let

$$F(x) = \int_a^x f(t) \, dt.$$

Then F is continuous over $[a, b]$, differentiable over $]a, b[$, and $F'(x) = f(x)$ for every $x \in \,]a, b[$. Therefore $G'(x) = F'(x)$ for every $x \in \,]a, b[$. Hence by Theorem 177 there exists $k \in \mathbf{K}$ such that

$$G(x) = F(x) + k.$$

Therefore

$$G(b) - G(a) = [F(b) + k] - [F(a) + k]$$

$$= F(b) - F(a)$$

$$= \int_a^b f(t)\, dt - \int_a^a f(t)\, dt$$

$$= \int_a^b f(t)\, dt. \quad \Box$$

EXERCISES

1 Prove that if $n \neq -1$, then

$$\int_a^b x^n\, dx = \frac{1}{n+1}(b^{n+1} - a^{n+1}).$$

2 Evaluate $\int_0^1 (2x + 1)^3\, dx$.

3 Let f be defined and bounded over $[a, b]$. A function G that is continuous over $[a, b]$ is said to be a *primitive* of f relative to $[a, b]$ iff

$$G'(x) = f(x) \qquad \text{for every} \quad x \in\,]a, b[.$$

Prove that if f is continuous over $[a, b]$, then f has a primitive relative to $[a, b]$.

4 *Strong version of the Fundamental Theorem of Integral Calculus.* Let f be defined and bounded over $[a, b]$. Prove that if $f \in \mathcal{R}[a, b]$, and if there exists a function F that is continuous over $[a, b]$, differentiable over $]a, b[$, and $F'(x) = f(x)$ for all $x \in\,]a, b[$, then

$$\int_a^b f(t)\, dt = F(b) - F(a).$$

[Hint: Use the mean value theorem for derivatives.]

5 Prove that if $k \neq 1$, then

$$\lim_n \left(\frac{1^k + 2^k + \cdots + n^k}{n^{k+1}} \right) = \frac{1}{k+1}.$$

> INFINITE SERIES

In this chapter our principal concern will be the representation of functions by means of infinite series. We shall also look into the questions of differentiating and integrating such functions by means of their series representations.

Basic Definitions and Theorems

We begin by studying infinite series of numbers.

201 DEFINITION

Let a be a sequence in $\mathbf{K}$. The formal sum

$$\sum_{i=1}^{\infty} a_i = a_1 + \cdots + a_n + \cdots$$

is called an *infinite series*. The numbers $a_1, a_2, \ldots$ are called the *terms* of the series. The sequence s in $\mathbf{K}$ defined by

$$s_n = \sum_{i=1}^{n} a_i = a_1 + \cdots + a_n$$

is called the *sequence of partial sums* associated with $\sum_{i=1}^{\infty} a_i$.

For example, $\sum_{i=1}^{\infty} 1/i^2$ is an infinite series. Its first term is 1, and its tenth term is $1/100$. The partial sums of the series are

$$s_1 = 1$$

$$s_2 = \tfrac{5}{4}$$

$$s_3 = \tfrac{49}{36},$$

$$s_n = 1 + \frac{1}{4} + \cdots + \frac{1}{n^2}.$$

As another example, $\sum_{i=5}^{\infty} 1/(i-3)$ is an infinite series. We shall follow the convention that the first four terms of this series are zero. That is,

$$\sum_{i=5}^{\infty} \frac{1}{i-3} = \sum_{i=1}^{\infty} a_i$$

where

$$a_i = \begin{cases} 0, & i = 1, 2, 3, 4, \\ \dfrac{1}{i-3}, & i \geq 5. \end{cases}$$

Therefore the sequence of partial sums is given by

$$s_1 = s_2 = s_3 = s_4 = 0,$$

$$s_5 = \tfrac{1}{2},$$

$$s_n = \frac{1}{2} + \cdots + \frac{1}{n}.$$

202 DEFINITION

Let s be the sequence of partial sums associated with the infinite series $\sum_{i=1}^{\infty} a_i$. The infinite series is said to be *convergent* and have the sum l

($l \in \mathbf{K}$) iff s is convergent and $\lim s_n = l$. The infinite series is said to be *divergent* iff s is divergent. We shall say that a divergent infinite series *has no sum*.

Consider the infinite series $\sum_{i=1}^{\infty} 1/2^i$. For this series

$$s_n = \frac{1}{2} + \frac{1}{2^2} + \cdots + \frac{1}{2^n},$$

so

$$\frac{1}{2} s_n = \frac{1}{2^2} + \cdots + \frac{1}{2^n} + \frac{1}{2^{n+1}}.$$

Hence

$$\frac{1}{2} s_n = \frac{1}{2} - \frac{1}{2^{n+1}},$$

so that

$$s_n = 1 - \frac{1}{2^n}.$$

Since $\lim s_n = 1$, we conclude that $\sum_{i=1}^{\infty} 1/2^i$ is a convergent infinite series whose sum is 1.

Next, consider the infinite series $\sum_{i=1}^{\infty} 1/i$. Note that

$$s_1 = 1 > \frac{1}{2},$$

$$s_2 = 1 + \frac{1}{2} > \frac{1}{2} + \frac{1}{2} = 2\left(\frac{1}{2}\right),$$

and that

$$s_4 = s_2 + \frac{1}{3} + \frac{1}{4} > 2\left(\frac{1}{2}\right) + \frac{1}{4} + \frac{1}{4} = 3\left(\frac{1}{2}\right).$$

If we take as induction hypothesis

$$s(2^k) > (k + 1)\left(\frac{1}{2}\right),\dagger$$

then

$$s(2^{k+1}) = s(2^k) + \frac{1}{2^k + 1} + \cdots + \frac{1}{2^{k+1}}$$

$$> (k + 1)\left(\frac{1}{2}\right) + 2^k\left(\frac{1}{2^{k+1}}\right),$$

$$= (k + 1)\left(\frac{1}{2}\right) + \frac{1}{2} = (k + 2)\left(\frac{1}{2}\right).$$

†When t is complicated, we shall denote the tth term of a sequence s by "$s(t)$".

Given any positive real number M, choose (Archimedean order) $n \in \mathbf{N}$ so that $n > 2M$. Then

$$s(2^n) > (n + 1)\left(\frac{1}{2}\right) > \frac{n}{2} > \frac{2M}{2} = M.$$

Hence s is not bounded, and so s is not convergent (Theorem 132). Therefore $\sum_{i=1}^{\infty} 1/i$ is a divergent infinite series.

Leaving out the first term of a sequence does not change its limit.

203 THEOREM

Let s be a sequence such that

$$\lim s_n = l.$$

If t is the sequence defined by

$$t_1 = 0,$$

$$t_n = s_{n-1}, n \geq 2,$$

then

$$\lim t_n = l.$$

Proof

Since $\lim s_n = l$, given $\varepsilon < 0$ there exists $n_\varepsilon \in \mathbf{N}$ such that

$$|s_n - l| < \varepsilon$$

for all $n \geq n_\varepsilon$. Let $m_\varepsilon = n_\varepsilon + 1$. If $n \geq m_\varepsilon$, then $n \geq 2$ and

$$n - 1 \geq m_\varepsilon - 1 = n_\varepsilon.$$

Hence

$$|t_n - l| = |s_{n-1} - l| < \varepsilon$$

for all $n \geq m_\varepsilon$. Therefore $\lim t_n = l$. $\square$

Our next theorem gives a necessary condition for convergence of an infinite series.

204 THEOREM

If $\sum_{i=1}^{\infty} a_i$ is convergent, then $\lim a_i = 0$.

Proof

Let s be the sequence of partial sums associated with $\sum_{i=1}^{\infty} a_i$, and let $t_1 = 0$, $t_n = s_{n-1}$, $n \geq 2$. Then

$$s_1 - t_1 = a_1 - 0 = a_1,$$

and

$$s_n - t_n = (a_1 + \cdots + a_n) - (a_1 + \cdots + a_{n-1}) = a_n, \qquad n \geq 2.$$

Moreover, since $\sum_{i=1}^{\infty} a_i$ is convergent, there exists $l \in \mathbf{K}$ such that $\lim s_n = l$. By Theorem 203, $\lim t_n = l$. Hence

$$\lim a_n = \lim(s_n - t_n) = \lim s_n - \lim t_n$$

$$= l - l = 0. \quad \square$$

Note carefully that the condition $\lim a_i = 0$ is not *sufficient* for convergence of $\sum_{i=1}^{\infty} a_i$; as we have already observed, $\sum_{i=1}^{\infty} 1/i$ is divergent.

If two sequences are eventually identical, then they have the same limit.

205 THEOREM

If $s_n = t_n$ for all $n > n_0$, and if $\lim s_n = l$, then $\lim t_n = l$.

Proof

Given $\varepsilon > 0$, there exists n_ε such that $|s_n - l| < \varepsilon$ for all $n \geq n_\varepsilon$. Let $m_\varepsilon = \max\{n_\varepsilon, n_0 + 1\}$. If $n \geq m_\varepsilon$, then $|t_n - l| = |s_n - l| < \varepsilon$. $\quad \square$

206 THEOREM

Let a and b be any two sequence in $\mathbf{K}$ such that $a_i = b_i$ for all but a finite number of $i \in \mathbf{N}$. Then $\sum_{i=1}^{\infty} a_i$ and $\sum_{i=1}^{\infty} b_i$ either both converge or both diverge.

Proof

Let s be the sequence of partial sums associated with $\sum_{i=1}^{\infty} a_i$, and let t be the sequence of partial sums associated with $\sum_{i=1}^{\infty} b_i$. Since $a_i = b_i$ for all but a finite number of $i \in \mathbf{N}$, there exists $n_0 \in \mathbf{N}$ such that $a_i = b_i$ for all $i > n_0$. Therefore

$$s_n - t_n = s_{n_0} - t_{n_0} \qquad \text{for all } n > n_0.$$

Hence

$$s_n = (s_{n_0} - t_{n_0}) + t_n$$

and

$$t_n = s_n - (s_{n_0} - t_{n_0})$$

for all $n > n_0$. If $\lim s_n = l$, then

$$\lim t_n = \lim s_n - (s_{n_0} - t_{n_0})$$
$$= l - (s_{n_0} - t_{n_0}).$$

Hence if s is convergent, so is t.

Similarly, if $\lim t_n = l'$, then

$$\lim s_n = \lim t_n + (s_{n_0} - t_{n_0})$$
$$= l' + (s_{n_0} - t_{n_0}).$$

Hence if t is convergent, so is s.

Therefore it cannot happen that s is convergent and t is not, or that t is convergent and s is not. $\square$

207 THEOREM

Let a be a sequence in $\mathbf{K}$, and let c be a nonzero real number. Then

$$\sum_{i=1}^{\infty} a_i \qquad \text{and} \qquad \sum_{i=1}^{\infty} ca_i$$

either both converge or both diverge.

Proof

If s and t are the sequences of partial sums associated with $\sum_{i=1}^{\infty} a_i$ and $\sum_{i=1}^{\infty} ca_i$, respectively, then

$$t_n = ca_i + \cdots + ca_n = c(a_1 + \cdots + a_n) = cs_n.$$

If $\lim s_n = l$, then

$$\lim t_n = c \lim s_n = cl,$$

and if

$$\lim t_n = l',$$

then

$$\lim s_n = c^{-1} \lim t_n = c^{-1}l'.$$

Therefore s and t both converge or both diverge. $\square$

EXERCISES

In Exercises 1 through 4, determine whether the given series is convergent or divergent. If convergent, find the sum.

1 $\displaystyle\sum_{i=1}^{\infty} \frac{i}{i+1}$.

2 $\displaystyle\sum_{i=1}^{\infty} \frac{1}{3^i}$.

3 $\displaystyle\sum_{i=1}^{\infty} \frac{1}{i(i+1)}$ $\left[\text{Hint}: \frac{1}{i(i+1)} = \frac{1}{i} - \frac{1}{i+1} \right]$.

4 $\displaystyle\sum_{i=1}^{\infty} \sin\frac{i\pi}{2}$.

5 State and prove a generalization of Theorem 203.

Series of Nonnegative Terms

As a general rule, it is quite difficult to apply Definition 202 directly to the problem of determining whether a given infinite series is convergent or divergent. The reason for this is that it is often next to impossible to find a manageable form for the sequence of partial sums. Tests for convergence and divergence that do not involve the sequence of partial sums can be devised (and we shall devise some in this section), but there is a price that must be paid: such tests give very little—if any—information concerning the *sum* of a convergent infinite series.

208 THEOREM   The Comparison Test

Let $\sum_{i=1}^{\infty} a_i$ and $\sum_{i=1}^{\infty} b_i$ be two series of nonnegative terms (i.e. $a_i \geq 0$ and $b_i \geq 0$ for every $i \in \mathbf{N}$).

[1] If there exists $n_0 \in \mathbf{N}$ such that $a_i \leq b_i$ for all $i \geq n_0$, and if $\sum_{i=1}^{\infty} b_i$ converges, then $\sum_{i=1}^{\infty} a_i$ converges.

[2] If there exists $n_0 \in \mathbf{N}$ such that $a_i \geq b_i$ for all $i \geq n_0$, and if $\sum_{i=1}^{\infty} b_i$ diverges, then $\sum_{i=1}^{\infty} a_i$ diverges.

Proof

Let

$$c_i = \begin{cases} 0 & \text{if } i < n_0 \\ a_n & \text{if } i \geq n_0, \end{cases}$$

and let

$$d_i = \begin{cases} 0 & \text{if } i < n_0 \\ b_n & \text{if } i \geq n_0. \end{cases}$$

[1] Assume that $\sum_{i=1}^{\infty} b_i$ converges, and that $a_i \leq b_i$ for all $i \geq n_0$. Then $c_i \leq d_i$ for all $i \in \mathbf{N}$, and it follows from Theorem 206 that $\sum_{i=1}^{\infty} d_i$ converges, say $\sum_{i=1}^{\infty} d_i = l$. Let s and t be the sequences of partial sums associated with $\sum_{i=1}^{\infty} c_i$ and $\sum_{i=1}^{\infty} d_i$, respectively. Since $c_i \geq 0$ and $d_i \geq 0$ for all $i \in \mathbf{N}$, it follows that both s and t are monotone-increasing sequences. Hence

$$l = \lim t_n = \text{lub}\{t_n : n \in \mathbf{N}\}.$$

But

$$s_n = c_1 + \cdots + c_n \leq d_1 + \cdots + d_n = t_n \leq l \qquad \text{for every} \quad n \in \mathbf{N}.$$

Therefore $s_n \leq l$ for every $n \in \mathbf{N}$, and so s is convergent (since it is monotone-increasing and bounded above). Hence $\sum_{i=1}^{\infty} c_i$ is convergent, from which it follows by Theorem 206 that $\sum_{i=1}^{\infty} a_i$ converges.

[2] Now assume that $\sum_{i=1}^{\infty} b_i$ diverges, and that $a_i \geq b_i$ for all $i \geq n_0$. Then $c_i \geq d_i$ for all $i \in \mathbf{N}$, and $\sum_{i=1}^{\infty} d_i$ diverges. As before, let s and t be the sequences of partial sums associated with $\sum_{i=1}^{\infty} c_i$ and $\sum_{i=1}^{\infty} d_i$, respectively. As before, these sequences are both monotone-increasing. Since $\sum_{i=1}^{\infty} d_i$ diverges, $\lim t_n$ does not exist. Hence

$$\{t_n : n \in \mathbf{N}\}$$

is not bounded above. But

$$s_n = c_1 + \cdots + c_n \geq d_1 + \cdots + d_n = t_n$$

for every $n \in \mathbf{N}$. Therefore $\{s_n : n \in \mathbf{N}\}$ is not bounded above, and, since s is monotone increasing, it follows that $\lim s_n$ does not exist. Hence $\sum_{i=1}^{\infty} c_i$ is divergent, and so $\sum_{i=1}^{\infty} a_i$ is divergent. $\square$

In order to apply the comparison test it is necessary (1) to have made a guess as to whether the series under test converges or diverges, and (2) to have a supply of series with which to compare the series under test. The former requires the experience that comes from practice, but the latter can be taken care of right now.

209 THEOREM   Geometric series

The infinite series $\sum_{i=1}^{\infty} r^i$ converges if $0 \le r < 1$ and diverges if $r \ge 1$.

Proof

[1] Assume that $0 \le r < 1$, and let

$$s_n = r + r^2 + \cdots + r^n.$$

Then

$$rs_n = r^2 + \cdots + r^n + r^{n+1}$$

from which it follows that

$$(1 - r)s_n = r - r^{n+1}.$$

Therefore

$$s_n = \frac{r}{1 - r} - \frac{1}{1 - r} r^{n+1}.$$

Since $0 \le r < 1$, $\lim r^{n+1} = \lim r^n = 0$, and so

$$\lim s_n = \frac{r}{1 - r}.$$

Therefore $\sum_{i=1}^{\infty} r^i$ is convergent [and has sum $r/(1 - r)$].

[2] Assume $r \ge 1$. Then $r^i \ge 1$ for every $i \in \mathbf{N}$, and so $\lim r^i \ne 0$. Therefore $\sum_{i=1}^{\infty} r^i$ is divergent. □

210 THEOREM   p-series

The infinite series $\sum_{i=1}^{\infty} 1/i^p$ converges if $p > 1$ and diverges if $0 \le p \le 1$.

Proof

[1] Let s be the sequence of partial sums associated with $\sum_{i=1}^{\infty} 1/i^p$. Assume that $p > 1$. Then

$$s_1 = 1$$

$$s_3 = 1 + \frac{1}{2^p} + \frac{1}{3^p}$$

$$s_3 \le 1 + \frac{1}{2^p} + \frac{1}{2^p} = 1 + \frac{1}{2^{p-1}}.$$

If we take as induction hypothesis

$$s(2^k - 1) \le 1 + \frac{1}{2^{p-1}} + \cdots + \left(\frac{1}{2^{p-1}}\right)^{k-1},$$

then

$$s(2^{k+1} - 1) = s(2^k - 1) + \frac{1}{(2^k)^p} + \frac{1}{(2^k + 1)^p} + \cdots + \frac{1}{(2^{k+1} - 1)^p}$$

$$\le s(2^k - 1) + \frac{2^k}{(2^k)^p} = s(2^k - 1) + \left(\frac{1}{2^k}\right)^{p-1}$$

$$\le 1 + \frac{1}{2^{p-1}} + \cdots + \left(\frac{1}{2^{p-1}}\right)^{k-1} + \left(\frac{1}{2^{p-1}}\right)^k.$$

Hence

$$s(2^m - 1) \le 1 + \left(\frac{1}{2^{p-1}}\right) + \cdots + \left(\frac{1}{2^{p-1}}\right)^{m-1} \qquad \text{for every} \quad m \in \mathbf{N}.$$

Now

$$1 + \frac{1}{2^{p-1}} + \cdots + \left(\frac{1}{2^{p-1}}\right)^{m-1} = \frac{1 - (1/2^{p-1})^m}{1 - (1/2^{p-1})}$$

$$= \frac{1}{1 - (1/2^{p-1})} - \frac{(1/2^{p-1})^m}{1 - (1/2^{p-1})}.$$

Since $p > 1$, $p - 1 > 0$, and so $2^{p-1} > 1$. Therefore $1/2^{p-1} < 1$, and it follows that

$$\frac{(1/2^{p-1})^m}{1 - (1/2^{p-1})} > 0 \qquad \text{for every} \quad m \in \mathbf{N}.$$

Therefore

$$s(2^m - 1) < \frac{1}{1 - (1/2^{p-1})} \qquad \text{for every} \quad m \in \mathbf{N}.$$

The sequence s is monotone-increasing because $1/i^p > 0$ for every $i \in \mathbf{N}$. Furthermore, given $n \in \mathbf{N}$, choose m so that $2^m > n + 1$. Then $2^m - 1 > n$, and so

$$s_n \le s(2^m - 1) < \frac{1}{1 - (1/2^{p-1})}.$$

Hence s is bounded above. Therefore s is convergent, from which it follows that $\sum_{i=1}^{\infty} 1/i^p$ is convergent.

[2] Assume that $0 \le p \le 1$. Then $i^p \le i$ for every $i \in \mathbf{N}$. Since $\sum_{i=1}^{\infty} 1/i$ diverges, it follows from the comparison test that $\sum_{i=1}^{\infty} 1/i^p$ diverges. $\square$

Consider the infinite series

$$\sum_{i=1}^{\infty} \frac{5}{i^2 + 2}.$$

Since $i^2 + 2 > i^2$ for every $i \in \mathbf{N}$,

$$\frac{1}{i^2 + 2} < \frac{1}{i^2} \qquad \text{for every} \quad i \in \mathbf{N}.$$

Now $\sum_{i=1}^{\infty} 1/i^2$ is a p-series with $p = 2$ and so is convergent. It follows from the comparison test that $\sum_{i=1}^{\infty} 1/(i^2 + 2)$ is convergent. Applying Theorem 207, we conclude that $\sum_{i=1}^{\infty} 5/(i^2 + 2)$ is convergent.

As a second example, consider

$$\sum_{i=1}^{\infty} \frac{1}{\sqrt{i + 2}}.$$

Now

$$i + 2 \le 2i \qquad \text{if} \quad i \ge 2.$$

Since $\sum_{i=1}^{\infty} 1/\sqrt{i}$ is a p-series with $p = \frac{1}{2}$, it is divergent. Therefore, by Theorem 207, $\sum_{i=1}^{\infty} 1/\sqrt{2i}$ is divergent. But

$$\frac{1}{\sqrt{i + 2}} \ge \frac{1}{\sqrt{2i}} \qquad \text{if} \quad i \ge 2,$$

and so, by the comparison test, $\sum_{i=1}^{\infty} 1/\sqrt{i + 2}$ is divergent.

Our next test is generally much easier to use than the comparison test. As the proof shows, however, if this test "works" for a convergent series, then comparison with a geometric series would also have worked. When this test "works" for divergence, then the limit of the nth term of the series is not zero, so that the series is *really* divergent. Finally, this test may fail to work at all.

But it *is* easy to use.

211 THEOREM   The Ratio Test

Let $\sum_{i=1}^{\infty} a_i$ be an infinite series of positive terms (i.e., $a_i > 0$ for every $i \in \mathbf{N}$). For each $n \in \mathbf{N}$ let

$$T_n = \frac{a_{n+1}}{a_n}.$$

[1] If $\lim T_n = l$ where $0 \le l < 1$, then $\sum_{i=1}^{\infty} a_i$ converges.

[2] If $\lim T_n = l$ where $l > 1$, or if T is monotone-increasing but not bounded above, then $\sum_{i=1}^{\infty} a_i$ diverges.

[3] If $\lim T_n = 1$, then $\sum_{i=1}^{\infty} a_i$ may either converge or diverge.

Proof

[1] Assume that $\lim T_n = l$ where $0 \le l < 1$. Let

$$\varepsilon_0 = \frac{1 - l}{2}.$$

Since $l < 1$ it follows that $\varepsilon_0 > 0$. Therefore there exists $n_0 \in \mathbf{N}$ such that

$$|T_n - l| < \varepsilon_0 \qquad \text{for all} \quad n \ge n_0.$$

In particular,

$$T_n < l + \varepsilon_0 \qquad \text{for all} \quad n \ge n_0.$$

Let $r = l + \varepsilon_0$. We then have

$$r = l + \varepsilon_0 = l + \frac{1 - l}{2} = \frac{l + 1}{2}.$$

But $l < 1$, so

$$r < \frac{1 + 1}{2} = 1.$$

Therefore $T_n < r$ for all $n \ge n_0$, and $r < 1$. In particular

$$T_{n_0} = \frac{a_{n_0 + 1}}{a_{n_0}} < r,$$

and so, since $a_{n_0} > 0$,

$$a_{n_0 + 1} < r a_{n_0}.$$

Similarly,

$$T_{n_0 + 1} = \frac{a_{n_0 + 2}}{a_{n_0 + 1}} < r,$$

and so

$$a_{n_0+2} < r a_{n_0+1} < r^2 a_{n_0}.$$

If we take as induction hypothesis

$$a_{n_0+k} < r^k a_{n_0},$$

then

$$T_{n_0+k} = \frac{a_{n_0+k+1}}{a_{n_0+k}} < r,$$

so

$$a_{n_0+k+1} < r a_{n_0+k} < r^{k+1} a_{n_0}.$$

Therefore

$$a_{n_0+j} < r^j a_{n_0} \qquad \text{for every} \quad j \in \mathbf{N}.$$

Now $\sum_{j=i}^{\infty} r^j$ converges, because it is a geometric series with $r < 1$. It then follows from Theorem 207 that $\sum_{j=1}^{\infty} a_{n_0} r^j$ is convergent. The comparison test then guarantees that $\sum_{j=i}^{\infty} a_{n_0+j}$ is convergent. Since

$$\sum_{i=1}^{\infty} a_i = (a_1 + \cdots + a_{n_0}) + \sum_{j=1}^{\infty} a_{n_0+j},$$

it follows that $\sum_{i=1}^{\infty} a_i$ is convergent.

[2] Now assume that $\lim T_n = l$ where $l > 1$. Let

$$\varepsilon_0 = \frac{l-1}{2}.$$

Then $\varepsilon_0 > 0$, so there exists $n_0 \in \mathbf{N}$ such that

$$|T_n - l| < \varepsilon_0 \qquad \text{for all} \quad n \geq n_0.$$

Therefore

$$l - \varepsilon_0 < T_n \qquad \text{for all} \quad n \geq n_0.$$

Since

$$l - \varepsilon_0 = l - \frac{l-1}{2} = \frac{l+1}{2} > 1,$$

we have

$$T_n > 1 \qquad \text{for all} \quad n \geq n_0.$$

In particular

$$T_{n_0} = \frac{a_{n_0+1}}{a_{n_0}} > 1,$$

and so

$$a_{n_0+1} > a_{n_0}.$$

Similarly

$$T_{n_0+1} = \frac{a_{n_0+2}}{a_{n_0+1}} > 1,$$

so $a_{n_0+2} > a_{n_0+1} > a_{n_0}$. If we take as induction hypothesis

$$a_{n_0+k} > a_{n_0},$$

then

$$T_{n_0+k} = \frac{a_{n_0+k+1}}{a_{n_0+k}} > 1$$

and so

$$a_{n_0+k+1} > a_{n_0+k} > a_{n_0}.$$

It follows that $a_{n_0+j} > a_{n_0}$ for every $j \in \mathbf{N}$. Since $a_{n_0} > 0$, it follows that $\lim a_i \neq 0$ (take $\varepsilon = a_{n_0}$). Therefore $\sum_{i=1}^{\infty} a_i$ is divergent (Theorem 204).

Now assume that T is monotone-increasing but not bounded above. Then there exists $n_0 \in \mathbf{N}$ such that

$$T_{n_0} > 1.$$

Since T is monotone-increasing, $T_n \geq T_{n_0}$ for all $n \geq n_0$. Therefore

$$T_n > 1 \qquad \text{for all} \quad n \geq n_0.$$

The remainder of the argument in this case is the same as that in the paragraph above.

[3] Finally, consider the series $\sum_{i-1}^{\infty} 1/i$. This series is known to diverge, and for it we have

$$T_n = \frac{1/(n+1)}{1/n} = \frac{n}{n+1}.$$

Therefore $\lim T_n = 1$. On the other hand the series $\sum_{i=1}^{\infty} 1/i^2$ is known to converge, and for this series we have

$$\lim T_n = \lim \frac{1/(n+1)^2}{1/n^2} = \lim \frac{n^2}{n^2+2n+1} = 1.$$

Hence if $\lim T_n = 1$, $\sum_{i=1}^{\infty} a_i$ may either converge or diverge. $\square$

For example, given the series $\sum_{i=1}^{\infty} 1/i!$, we have†

$$T_n = \frac{1/(n+1)!}{1/n!} = \frac{n!}{(n+1)!} = \frac{1}{n+1}.$$

Therefore $\lim T_n = 0$, and so $\sum_{i=1}^{\infty} 1/i!$ converges.

Consider the infinite series $\sum_{i=1}^{\infty} 3^i/i^3$. For this series

$$T_n = \frac{3^{n+1}/(n+1)^3}{3^n/n^3} = 3\frac{n^3}{n^3 + 3n^2 + 3n + 1}.$$

Since $\lim T_n = 3$, we conclude that the given series is divergent.

EXERCISES

In Exercises 1 through 8, determine whether the given series converges or diverges.

1 $\sum_{i=1}^{\infty} \dfrac{|\sin i|}{i^3}.$

2 $\sum_{i=1}^{\infty} \dfrac{2+1/i}{i^2}.$

3 $\sum_{i=1}^{\infty} \dfrac{4^i}{i^3}.$

4 $\sum_{i=1}^{\infty} \dfrac{i}{2^i}.$

5 $\sum_{i=3}^{\infty} \dfrac{1}{(\log_{10} i)^i}.$

6 $\sum_{i=1}^{\infty} \dfrac{3^i}{i!}.$

7 $\sum_{i=1}^{\infty} \dfrac{2^i \cdot i!}{(2i)!}.$

8 $\sum_{i=1}^{\infty} \dfrac{1}{i^2+1}.$

9 Prove that if $\lim a_i = l$, then $\sum_{i=1}^{\infty} (a_i)^i$ converges if $0 \le l < 1$, and diverges if $l > 1$.

10 Let $\sum_{i=1}^{\infty} a_i$ be a series of nonnegative terms, let $\sum_{i=1}^{\infty} b_i$ be a series of positive terms, and let $\lim a_i/b_i = l$. Prove that if $l < 1$ and $\sum_{i=1}^{\infty} b_i$ is convergent, then $\sum_{i=1}^{\infty} a_i$ is convergent. Also prove that if $l > 1$ and $\sum_{i=1}^{\infty} b_i$ is divergent, then $\sum_{i=1}^{\infty} a_i$ is divergent.

11 For a given open interval $I =]a, b[$ we shall denote the number $b - a$ by $l(I)$, read "the length of I."

A set S of real numbers is said to be a set of *measure zero* iff for each $\varepsilon > 0$ there exists a countable set $\{I_1, I_2, \ldots\}$ of open intervals such that

$$S \subset \cup \{I_j : j = 1, 2, \ldots\}$$

and

$$\sum_j l(I_j) < \varepsilon.$$

† $0! = 1$, $1! = 1$, $(i+1)! = (i+1) \cdot i!$, $i \in \mathbf{N}$.

Prove that every countable set of real numbers is a set of measure zero. (In particular, the set Q of all rational numbers is a set of measure zero.)

Absolute Convergence

In order to bring the results of the preceding section to bear on the general problem of series convergence, we introduce the following concept.

212 DEFINITION

An infinite series $\sum_{i=1}^{\infty} a_i$ is said to be *absolutely convergent* iff the series $\sum_{i=1}^{\infty} |a_i|$ is convergent. An infinite series that is convergent but not absolutely convergent is said to be *conditionally convergent*.

Note that if $\sum_{i=1}^{\infty} a_i$ is a series of nonnegative terms, then $|a_i| = a_i$ for every $i \in N$. Therefore such a series is absolutely convergent if and only if it is convergent. Similarly, if $a_i < 0$ for every $i \in N$, then

$$|a_i| = (-1)a_i \qquad \text{for every} \quad i \in N,$$

and so $\sum_{i=1}^{\infty} a_i$ is absolutely convergent if and only if it is convergent (Theorem 207). Hence a conditionally convergent series must have at least one negative term and at least one positive term.

In fact, it must have several of each kind.

213 THEOREM

If $\sum_{i=1}^{\infty} a_i$ is conditionally convergent, then $a_i < 0$ for infinitely many $i \in N$, and $a_i > 0$ for infinitely many $i \in N$.

Proof

Assume $\sum_{i=1}^{\infty} a_i$ converges conditionally. Suppose $a_i < 0$ for only a finite number of $i \in N$. Then there is an integer n_0 such that

$$a_i \geq 0 \qquad \text{for all} \quad i \geq n_0.$$

Hence

$$|a_i| = a_i \qquad \text{for all} \quad i \geq n_0.$$

Therefore $\sum_{i=1}^{\infty} |a_i|$ is convergent (Theorem 206), so $\sum_{i=1}^{\infty} a_i$ is absolutely convergent, a contradiction. Hence $a_i < 0$ for infinitely many $i \in N$.

Suppose $a_i > 0$ for only a finite number of $i \in \mathbf{N}$. Then there is an integer n_1 such that

$$a_i \leq 0 \qquad \text{for all} \quad i \geq n_1.$$

It follows that

$$|a_i| = -a_i = (-1)a_i \qquad \text{for all} \quad i \geq n_1.$$

But $\sum_{i=1}^{\infty} (-1)a_i$ is convergent (Theorem 207), so $\sum_{i=1}^{\infty} |a_i|$ is convergent, a contradiction. Therefore $a_i > 0$ for infinitely many $i \in \mathbf{N}$. $\square$

By the way, an absolutely convergent series *is* convergent.

214 THEOREM

If $\sum_{i=1}^{\infty} a_i$ converges absolutely, then $\sum_{i=1}^{\infty} a_i$ converges.

Proof

Let

$$c_i = \begin{cases} a_i & \text{if} \quad a_i \geq 0 \\ 0 & \text{if} \quad a_i < 0, \end{cases}$$

and

$$d_i = \begin{cases} a_i & \text{if} \quad a_i < 0 \\ 0 & \text{if} \quad a_i \geq 0. \end{cases}$$

Let s be the sequence of partial sums associated with $\sum_{i=1}^{\infty} a_i$, s' with $\sum_{i=1}^{\infty} |a_i|$, u with $\sum_{i=1}^{\infty} c_i$, and v with $\sum_{i=1}^{\infty} d_i$. The sequences s' and u are then monotone-increasing, while v is monotone-decreasing. Hence $-v$ is monotone-increasing.

Now

$$s_n = u_n + v_n \qquad \text{for every} \quad n \in \mathbf{N},$$

and

$$s'_n = u_n - v_n = u_n + (-v_n) \qquad \text{for every} \quad n \in \mathbf{N}.$$

Also

$$u_n \geq 0 \qquad \text{for every} \quad n \in \mathbf{N},$$

and

$$-v_n \geq 0 \qquad \text{for every} \quad n \in \mathbf{N}.$$

Therefore

$$u_n \leq s'_n \qquad \text{for every} \quad n \in \mathbf{N}$$

and

$$-v_n \leq s'_n \qquad \text{for every} \quad n \in \mathbf{N}.$$

Since $\sum_{i=1}^{\infty} a_i$ is absolutely convergent, $\sum_{i=1}^{\infty} |a_i|$ is convergent, and so there exists $l \in \mathbf{K}$ such that $\lim s_n' = l$. Since s' is monotone-increasing, $l = \text{lub}\{s_n' : n \in \mathbf{N}\}$. Hence

$$s_n' \le l \qquad \text{for every} \quad n \in \mathbf{N}.$$

Therefore

$$u_n \le l \qquad \text{for every} \quad n \in \mathbf{N},$$

and

$$-v_n \le l \qquad \text{for every} \quad n \in \mathbf{N}.$$

It follows that

$$v_n \ge -l \quad \text{for every} \quad n \in \mathbf{N}.$$

Therefore u is monotone-increasing and bounded above, while v is monotone-decreasing and bounded below. Hence u and v are both convergent, say $\lim u_n = l_1$ and $\lim v_n = l_2$. We then have

$$\lim s_n = \lim(u_n + v_n)$$
$$= \lim u_n + \lim v_n$$
$$= l_1 + l_2.$$

Therefore s is convergent, and so $\sum_{i=1}^{\infty} a_i$ is convergent. $\square$

215 COROLLARY

If $\sum_{i=1}^{\infty} a_i$ is absolutely convergent, then

$$\left| \sum_{i=1}^{\infty} a_i \right| \le \sum_{i=i}^{\infty} |a_i|.$$

Proof

Using the notation introduced in the proof of Theorem 214 we have

$$\left| \sum_{i=1}^{\infty} a_i \right| = |\lim s_n| = |l_1 + l_2|$$
$$\le |l_1| + |l_2|$$
$$= l_1 + (-l_2)$$
$$= \lim u_n + \lim(-v_n)$$
$$= \lim(u_n - v_n)$$

$$\left| \sum_{i=1}^{\infty} a_i \right| \leq \lim s_n'$$

$$= \sum_{i=1}^{\infty} |a_i|. \quad \square$$

A given infinite series containing both positive and negative terms can be tested for absolute convergence by applying the methods of the preceding section to the series of absolute values. If the latter converges, then the given series is, of course, absolutely convergent, and that's that. But if the absolute value series should *diverge*, then the given series may either converge conditionally or diverge. The following test is often useful in resolving such questions.

216 THEOREM   Alternating Series Test

If $a_i \geq 0$ for every $i \in \mathbf{N}$, if $a_{i+1} \leq a_i$ for every $i \in \mathbf{N}$, and if $\lim a_i = 0$, then $\sum_{i=1}^{\infty} (-1)^{i+1} a_i$ is convergent.

Proof

Let s be the sequence of partial sums associated with $\sum_{i=1}^{\infty} (-1)^{i+1} a_i$, and let

$$u_n = s_{2n} \quad \text{for every} \quad n \in \mathbf{N}.$$

Since $a_{i+1} \leq a_i$ for every $i \in \mathbf{N}$, it follows that

$$u_n = s_{2n} = (a_1 - a_2) + \cdots + (a_{2n-1} - a_{2n}) \geq 0$$

for every $n \in \mathbf{N}$, and that

$$u_{n+1} - u_n = s_{2(n+1)} - s_{2n}$$

$$= (a_1 - a_2 + \cdots - a_{2n} + a_{2n+1} - a_{2n+2})$$

$$- (a_1 - a_2 + \cdots - a_{2n})$$

$$= a_{2n+1} - a_{2n+2} \geq 0$$

for every $n \in \mathbf{N}$. Therefore u is a monotone-increasing sequence of nonnegative terms.

Furthermore

$$u_n = s_{2n} = a_1 - (a_2 - a_3) - \cdots - (a_{2n-2} - a_{2n-1}) - a_{2n} \leq a_1$$

for every $n \in \mathbf{N}$. Since u is monotone-increasing and bounded above by a_1, it follows that there exists $l \in \mathbf{K}$ such that

$$\lim u_n = l.$$

As a matter of fact, $l = \text{lub}\{u_n : n \in \mathbf{N}\}$, so that

$$0 \le l \le a_1;$$

this fact will be needed to prove Corollary 217. Now let $v_n = s_{2n+1}$ for every $n \in \mathbf{N}$. Then $v_n = s_{2n} + a_{2n+1} = u_n + a_{2n+1}$, from which it follows that

$$\lim v_n = \lim(u_n + a_{2n+1})$$

$$= \lim u_n + \lim a_{2n+1}$$

$$= l + 0,$$

since, by hypothesis, $\lim a_i = 0$.

We shall now show that $\lim s_n = l$. Given $\varepsilon > 0$, choose n_1 so that

$$|u_n - l| < \varepsilon \qquad \text{for all} \quad n \ge n_1,$$

and choose n_2 so that

$$|v_n - l| < \varepsilon \qquad \text{for all} \quad n \ge n_2.$$

Let $n_\varepsilon = \max\{2n_1, 2n_2 + 1\}$.

If $n \ge n_\varepsilon$, then either n is even or n is odd, and $n \ge 3$. If n is even, then $n = 2k$ for some $k \in \mathbf{N}$, so

$$2k \ge n_\varepsilon \ge 2n_1.$$

Therefore $k \ge n_1$, and so

$$|s_n - l| = |s_{2k} - l| = |u_k - l| < \varepsilon.$$

If n is odd, then $n = 2k + 1$ for some $k \in \mathbf{N}$ so

$$2k + 1 \ge n_0 \ge 2n_2 + 1.$$

Therefore $k \ge n_2$, and so

$$|s_n - l| = |s_{2k+1} - l| = |v_k - l| < \varepsilon.$$

It follows that

$$|s_n - l| < \varepsilon \qquad \text{for all} \quad n \ge n_\varepsilon.$$

Therefore $\sum_{i=1}^{\infty} (-1)^{i+1} a_i$ is convergent and has sum l. Furthermore, $0 \le l \le a_1$. $\square$

217 COROLLARY

Let $\sum_{i=1}^{\infty} (-1)^{i+1} a_i$ be an infinite series with $a_i \ge 0$ for every $i \in \mathbf{N}$, $a_{i+1} \le a_i$ for every $i \in \mathbf{N}$, and $\lim a_i = 0$. If l is the sum of this series, and if s is the sequence of partial sums associated with the series, then

$$|l - s_n| \leq a_{n+1} \qquad \text{for every} \quad n \in \mathbf{N}.$$

Proof

For given $n \in \mathbf{N}$ we have

$$l - s_n = \sum_{i=1}^{\infty} (-1)^{i+1} a_i - (a_1 - a_2 + \cdots + (-1)^{n+1} a_n)$$

$$= \sum_{i=n+1}^{\infty} (-1)^{i+1} a_i$$

$$= \sum_{j=1}^{\infty} (-1)^{n+j+1} a_{n+j}$$

$$= (-1)^n \sum_{j=1}^{\infty} (-1)^{j+1} a_{n+j}.$$

Therefore

$$|l - s_n| = \left| \sum_{j=1}^{\infty} (-1)^{j+1} a_{n+j} \right|.$$

Now $\sum_{j=1}^{\infty} (-1)^{j+1} a_{n+j}$ satisfies the hypothesis of the alternating series test. Hence its sum l_n satisfies the inequality $0 \leq l_n \leq a_{n+1}$ (this follows from the last sentence in the proof of Theorem 216). Therefore

$$|l - s_n| = \left| \sum_{j=1}^{\infty} (-1)^{j+1} a_{n+j} \right| = |l_n| = l_n \leq a_{n+1}$$

for every $n \in \mathbf{N}$. $\square$

Consider the series

$$\sum_{i=1}^{\infty} \frac{(-1)^{i+1}}{i}.$$

Since $1/i > 0$ for every $i \in \mathbf{N}$, and $\lim 1/i = 0$, it follows from the alternating series test that the given series is convergent. Since

$$\sum_{i-1}^{\infty} \left| \frac{(-1)^{i+1}}{i} \right| = \sum_{i=1}^{\infty} \frac{1}{i}$$

is divergent, it follows that

$$\sum_{i=1}^{\infty} \frac{(-1)^{i+1}}{i}$$

converges conditionally. The sum of this series differs from 1 by no more than $\frac{1}{2}$ (i.e. is in the interval $[\frac{1}{2}, \frac{3}{2}]$), from $1 - \frac{1}{2} = \frac{1}{2}$ by no more than

$\frac{1}{3}$ (i.e. is in the interval $[\frac{1}{6}, \frac{5}{6}]$), from $\frac{1}{2} + \frac{1}{3} = \frac{5}{6}$ by no more than $\frac{1}{4}$ (i.e. is in the interval $[\frac{7}{12}, \frac{13}{12}]$), and so on.

EXERCISES

In Exercises 1 through 5, determine whether the given infinite series is absolutely convergent, conditionally convergent, or divergent.

1   $\displaystyle\sum_{i=1}^{\infty} \frac{(-1)^{i+1}}{i^{1/3} + 1}$.

2   $\displaystyle\sum_{i=1}^{\infty} \frac{(-1)^{i+1} \cos(\pi/i)}{i^{\pi/2}}$.

3   $\displaystyle\sum_{i=1}^{\infty} \frac{(-1)^{i+1}}{i^{4/3} + 1}$.

4   $\displaystyle\sum_{i=1}^{\infty} \frac{(-3)^i}{i!}$.

5   $\displaystyle\sum_{i=1}^{\infty} (-1)^{i+1}(\sqrt{i+1} - \sqrt{i})$.

6   Prove that if $\sum_{i=1}^{\infty} a_i$ converges absolutely, then $\sum_{i=1}^{\infty} a_i^2$ is convergent.

7   Prove that if

$$\lim \frac{|a_i|}{|b_i|} = l < 1,$$

and if $\sum_{i=1}^{\infty} b_i$ is absolutely convergent, then $\sum_{i=1}^{\infty} a_i$ is absolutely convergent.

8   ▷ Prove that if the *ratio test* says that $\sum_{i=1}^{\infty} |a_i|$ diverges, then $\sum_{i=1}^{\infty} a_i$ diverges. [Hint: Re-examine the proof of Theorem 211.]

Infinite Series of Functions

We now extend the notion of infinite series to provide for series whose terms are functions.

218 DEFINITION

Let u be a sequence of functions each of which is defined over the same set $S \subset \mathbf{K}$. The formal sum

$$\sum_{i=1}^{\infty} u_i = u_1 + u_2 + \cdots + u_i + \cdots$$

is called an *infinite series of functions*. The subset C of S defined by

$$C = \left\{ x \in S : \sum_{i=1}^{\infty} u_i(x) \text{ converges} \right\}$$

is called the *domain of convergence* of $\sum_{i=1}^{\infty} u_i$. If $C \neq \varnothing$, the function ϕ defined by

$$\phi(x) = \sum_{i=1}^{\infty} u_i(x), \qquad x \in C$$

is called the *sum function* of $\sum_{i=1}^{\infty} u_i$. If $C \neq \varnothing$, then $\sum_{i=1}^{\infty} u_i$ *has no sum function*.

By way of an example, consider the infinite series $\sum_{i=1}^{\infty} x^i$. Applying the ratio test to the series $\sum_{i=1}^{\infty} |x^i|$, we have $T_n = |x|$, and so $\lim T_n = |x|$. Therefore $\sum_{i=1}^{\infty} x^i$ converges (absolutely) for all x with $|x| < 1$ and diverges (see Exercise 8, p. 178) for all x with $|x| > 1$. Since both $\sum_{i=1}^{\infty} 1$ and $\sum_{i=1}^{\infty} (-1)^i$ are divergent (why?), it follows that the domain of convergence of $\sum_{i=1}^{\infty} x^i$ is $]-1, 1[$.

Consider $\sum_{i=1}^{\infty} (\cos^i x)/i$. Applying the ratio test to the series $\sum_{i=1}^{\infty} |(\cos^i x)/i|$ we have

$$T_n = |\cos x| \frac{i}{i+1}.$$

Therefore $\lim T_n = |\cos x|$, and so the given series $\sum_{i=1}^{\infty} (\cos^i x)/i$ converges (absolutely) for all x with $|\cos x| < 1$. Since $|\cos x| > 1$ is impossible, the only remaining case is $|\cos x| = 1$. We note that $\sum_{i=1}^{\infty} 1/i$ is divergent, while $\sum_{i=1}^{\infty} (-1)^i/i$ is (conditionally) convergent. Therefore the domain of convergence is

$$\{ x \in \mathbf{K} : -1 \leq \cos x < 1 \} = \{ x \in \mathbf{K} : \cos x \neq 1 \}$$

$$= \{ x \in \mathbf{K} : x \neq 2j\pi, j \in \mathbf{Z} \}$$

EXERCISES

In Exercises 1 through 6, find the domain of convergence of the given series.

1    $\displaystyle\sum_{i=1}^{\infty} \frac{x^i}{i!}.$

2    $\displaystyle\sum_{i=1}^{\infty} i!x^i.$

3    $\displaystyle\sum_{i=1}^{\infty} \left(\frac{x-1}{i}\right)^i.$

4    $\displaystyle\sum_{i=1}^{\infty} \frac{(x+1)^i}{i \cdot 2^i}.$

5    $\displaystyle\sum_{i=1}^{\infty} \frac{2^{ix}}{i}.$

6    $\displaystyle\sum_{i=1}^{\infty} \frac{2^i \cdot i!}{(2i)!}x^i.$

7 ▷ *Definition.* Let f be a sequence of functions each of which is defined over the same set $C \subset \mathbf{K}$ and let ϕ be a function defined over C. We shall say that the sequence f *converges to ϕ over C* iff

$$\lim f_n(x) = \phi(x) \qquad \text{for every} \quad x \in C.$$

[1] Prove that f converges to ϕ over C iff for each $x \in S$ and for every $\varepsilon > 0$ there exists $n_{\varepsilon,x} \in \mathbf{N}$ such that

$$|f_n(x) - \phi(x)| < \varepsilon \qquad \text{for every} \quad n \geq n_{\varepsilon,x}.$$

[2] Let $\sum_{i=1}^{\infty} u_i$ be an infinite series of functions with domain of convergence C, let

$$f_n(x) = \sum_{i=1}^{n} u_i(x), \qquad n \in \mathbf{N} \quad \text{and} \quad x \in C,$$

and let ϕ be a function defined over C. Prove that ϕ is the sum function of $\sum_{i=1}^{\infty} u_i$ if and only if the sequence f converges to ϕ over C. (The sequence f is called the *sequence of partial sums* of $\sum_{i=1}^{\infty} u_i$.)

8   Give an example of a sequence f of functions, each of which is continuous over $[-1, 1]$, but such that f converges over $[-1, 1]$ to a function that is not continuous over $[-1, 1]$.

Power Series

We shall restrict our attention from now on to a particular kind of infinite series of functions. These series are of interest because of the many pleasant properties they enjoy with respect to domain of convergence and differentiation and integration of the sum function.

219 DEFINITION

A *power series* in powers of $(x - a)$ is a series of the form

$$c_0 + \sum_{i=1}^{\infty} c_i(x - a)^i$$

where $a \in \mathbf{K}$, $c_0 \in \mathbf{K}$, and c is a sequence in $\mathbf{K}$.

As a matter of convenience, we shall write the power series

$$c_0 + \sum_{i=1}^{\infty} c_i(x - a)^i$$

in the form

$$\sum_{i=0}^{\infty} c_i(x - a)^i,$$

with the understanding that the latter has the value c_0 when $x = a$. Let us also agree, just for the record, that the sequence of partial sums of a power series is given by

$$f_n(x) = c_0 + \sum_{i=1}^{n} c_i(x - a)^i, \qquad n \in \mathbf{N}.$$

220 LEMMA

If a power series $\sum_{i=0}^{\infty} c_i(x - a)^i$ converges for $x = x_1 \neq a$, then it converges absolutely for all x with

$$|x - a| < |x_1 - a|.$$

Proof

Since $\sum_{i=1}^{\infty} c_i(x_1 - a)^i$ converges, it follows that $\lim c_i(x_1 - a)^i = 0$. Therefore there exists $n_0 \in \mathbf{N}$ such that

$$|c_i(x_1 - a)^i| < 1 \qquad \text{for every} \quad n \geq n_0.$$

Let x be any real number such that

$$|x - a| < |x_1 - a|.$$

Then for every $i \geq n_0$,

$$|c_i(x - a)^i| = |c_i| \cdot |x - a|^i$$

$$= |c_i| \cdot |x_1 - a|^i \frac{|x - a|^i}{|x_1 - a|^i}$$

$$< \frac{|x - a|^i}{|x_1 - a|^i} = r_0^i$$

where

$$r_0 = \frac{|x - a|}{|x_1 - a|} < 1.$$

But $\sum_{i=1}^{\infty} r_0^i$ is a convergent geometric series, and so, by the comparison test, $\sum_{i=0}^{\infty} |c_i(x - a)^i|$ is convergent. Therefore $\sum_{i=0}^{\infty} c_i(x - a)^i$ converges absolutely. $\square$

221 THEOREM

For a given power series $\sum_{i=0}^{\infty} c_i(x - a)^i$, exactly one of the following is true:

[1] The series converges for $x = a$ and diverges for all $x \neq a$.

[2] There exists a positive real number r such that the series converges for all x with $|x - a| < r$ and diverges for all x with $|x - a| > r$.

[3] The series converges absolutely for all $x \in \mathbf{K}$.

Proof

It is clear that at most one of [1], [2], [3] can hold for a given power series. We shall show that at least one of them holds.

Let

$$S = \{k > 0 : \sum_{i=0}^{\infty} c_i(x - a)^i \text{ converges absolutely for all } x \text{ with } |x - a| < k\}.$$

[1] Assume $S = \emptyset$. If $\sum_{i=1}^{\infty} c_i(x - a)^i$ were convergent for $x = x_1$ with $x_1 \neq a$, then, by Lemma 220, $\sum_{i=1}^{\infty} c_i(x - a)^i$ would converge absolutely for all x with $|x - a| < |x_1 - a|$, and so $|x_1 - a|$ would belong to S. This contradicts the assumption that $S = \emptyset$, and so we conclude that $\sum_{i=0}^{\infty} c_i(x - a)^i$ diverges for all x with $x \neq a$. If $x = a$, $\sum_{i=0}^{\infty} c_i(x - a)^i$ is convergent with sum c_0. Therefore [1] holds.

[2] Assume that $S \neq \emptyset$ and that S is bounded above. Let

$$r = \text{lub } S.$$

Since all members of S are positive, it follows that $r > 0$. Moreover, if $|x_1 - a| < r$, then there exists $k \in S$ such that

$$|x_1 - a| < k \leq r,$$

so that, by definition of S, the series converges absolutely for $x = x_1$.

If $|x_1 - a| > r$, then $|x_1 - a| \notin S$, so $\sum_{i=0}^{\infty} |c_1(x - a)^i|$ diverges for at least one x with $|x - a| < |x_1 - a|$. If $\sum_{i=0}^{\infty} c_i(x - a)^i$ were convergent for $x = x_1$, then, by Lemma 220, it would be absolutely convergent for every x with $|x - a| < |x_1 - a|$, and so $\sum_{i=0}^{\infty} |c_i(x - a)^i|$ would converge for every x with $|x - a| < |x_1 - a|$, a contradiction. Hence $\sum_{i=0}^{\infty} c_i(x - a)^i$ is divergent for $x = x_1$. Therefore [3] holds. $\square$

[3] Assume that $S \neq \varnothing$ and that S is not bounded above. Then given $x_1 \in \mathbf{K}$ there exists $k \in S$ such that $k > |x_1 - a|$. Since $k \in S$, $\sum_{i=0}^{\infty} c_i(x - a)^i$ is absolutely convergent for all x with $|x - a| < k$. In particular, the series is absolutely convergent for $x = x_1$. Since x_1 was *chosen arbitrarily*, it follows that the series is absolutely convergent for every $x \in \mathbf{K}$. Therefore [2] holds. $\square$

The number r referred to in part [2] of Theorem 221 is called the *radius of convergence* of the power series. In case [1] we say that the radius of convergence is *zero*, and in case [3] we say that the radius of convergence is *infinite*.

In many instances, the ratio test can be used to find the radius of convergence of a power series. For example, the discussion in the preceding section shows that the series $\sum_{i=0}^{\infty} x^i$ has 1 as its radius of convergence.

As indicated in Exercise 7, p. 180, in the ordinary kind of convergence of a sequence of functions, the integer $n_{\varepsilon,x}$ that "works" for a given ε generally depends not only on ε but also on the particular point x at which the limit is being considered. If it should happen that $n_{\varepsilon,x}$ is actually independent of x, then the convergence is said to be *uniform*.

222 DEFINITION

A sequence f of functions converging to a function ϕ over a set S is said to converge *uniformly* over a set $E \subset S$ iff for every $\varepsilon > 0$ there exists $n_\varepsilon \in \mathbf{N}$ such that

$$|f_n(x) - \phi(x)| < \varepsilon$$

for all $x \in E$ and for all $n \geq n_\varepsilon$.

A uniformly convergent sequence of continuous functions has a continuous limit.

223 THEOREM

If f is a sequence of functions each of which is continuous relative to the same set E, and if f converges uniformly to ϕ over E, then ϕ is continuous relative to E. .

Proof

Let $a \in E$. Since f converges uniformly to ϕ over E, given $\varepsilon > 0$ there exists $n_\varepsilon \in \mathbf{N}$ such that

$$|f_n(x) - \phi(x)| < \tfrac{1}{3}\varepsilon$$

for every $x \in E$ and for every $n \geq n_\varepsilon$. Since f_{n_ε} is continuous at a, there exists $\delta > 0$ such that

$$|f_{n_\varepsilon}(x) - f_{n_\varepsilon}(a)| < \tfrac{1}{3}\varepsilon$$

for all $x \in E$ with $|x - a| < \delta$. Hence if $x \in E$ and $|x - a| < \delta$, then

$$|\phi(x) - \phi(a)| \leq |\phi(x) - f_{n_\varepsilon}(x)| + |f_{n_\varepsilon}(x) - f_{n_\varepsilon}(a)| + |f_{n_\varepsilon}(a) - \phi(a)|$$

$$< \tfrac{1}{3}\varepsilon + \tfrac{1}{3}\varepsilon + \tfrac{1}{3}\varepsilon = \varepsilon.$$

Therefore ϕ is continuous at a. $\square$

The notion of uniform convergence is extended to infinite series in the usual way—via the sequence of partial sums.

224 DEFINITION

An infinite series of functions $\sum_{i=1}^{\infty} u_i$ with domain of convergence C and sum function ϕ is said to *converge uniformly* over a set $E \subset C$ iff the sequence defined by

$$f_n(x) = \sum_{i=1}^{n} u_i(x)$$

converges uniformly to ϕ over E.

Our next theorem establishes a kind of uniform comparison test for series of functions.

225 THEOREM   Weierstrass M-test

Let $\sum_{i=1}^{\infty} u_i$ be an infinite series of functions. If there exists a convergent series of nonnegative terms $\sum_{i=1}^{\infty} M_i$, a positive integer n_0, and a set

$E \subset \mathbf{K}$ such that

$$|u_i(x)| \leq M_i$$

for all $x \in E$ and for all $i \geq n_0$, then $\sum_{i=1}^{\infty} u_i$ converges absolutely and uniformly over E.

Proof

The assertion concerning absolute convergence follows readily from the comparison test.

Let $l = \sum_{i=1}^{\infty} M_i$. Given $\varepsilon > 0$ there exists $j_0 \in \mathbf{N}$ such that $|l - \sum_{i=1}^{n} M_i| < \varepsilon$ for all $n \geq j_0$. But

$$l - \sum_{i=1}^{n} M_i = \sum_{i=n+1}^{\infty} M_i.$$

Hence

$$\sum_{i=n+1}^{\infty} M_i < \varepsilon \qquad \text{for all} \quad n \geq j_0.$$

Let $\phi(x) = \sum_{i=1}^{\infty} u_i(x)$ for every $x \in E$, and let $p_0 = \max\{n_0, j_0\}$. Then for every $n \geq p_0$ and for every $x \in E$,

$$\left| \phi(x) - \sum_{i=1}^{n} u_i(x) \right| = \left| \sum_{i=1}^{\infty} u_i(x) - \sum_{i=1}^{n} u_i(x) \right| = \left| \sum_{i=n+1}^{\infty} u_i(x) \right|$$

$$\leq \sum_{i=n+1}^{\infty} |u_i(x)| \qquad \text{C215}$$

$$\leq \sum_{i=n+1}^{\infty} M_n < \varepsilon.$$

Therefore $\sum_{i=1}^{\infty} u_i$ converges uniformly over E. $\square$

A power series is uniformly convergent over every closed interval contained in its domain of convergence.

226 THEOREM

If $\sum_{i=1}^{\infty} c_i(x - a)^i$ is convergent for $|x - a| < r$, and if $0 < r_1 < r$, then the series is uniformly convergent over $[a - r_1, a + r_1]$.

Proof

Let $M_i = |c_i| r_1^i$, $i = 0, 1, \ldots$. Then

$$\sum_{i=0}^{\infty} |c_i| \cdot r_1^i = \sum_{i=0}^{\infty} |c_i| \cdot |(r_1 + a) - a|^i,$$

and $|(r_1 + a) - a| = r_1 < r$. Therefore $\sum_{i=0}^{\infty} M_i$ is convergent. Moreover, if $|x - a| \leq r_1$, then

$$|c_i(x - a)^i| \leq |c_i|r_1^i, \qquad i = 0, 1, \ldots.$$

Hence, by the Weierstrass M-test, $\sum_{i=0}^{\infty} c_i(x - a)^i$ is uniformly convergent over

$$\{x \in \mathbf{K} : |x - a| \leq r_1\} = [a - r_1, a + r_1]. \quad \square$$

EXERCISES

In Exercises 1 through 4, find the domain of convergence of the given power series.

1    $\displaystyle\sum_{i=0}^{\infty} \frac{(x - 3)^i}{i + 2}.$
     2    $\displaystyle\sum_{i=0}^{\infty} (-1)^i(i + 1)!(x - 1)^i.$

3    $\displaystyle\sum_{i=0}^{\infty} \frac{(x + \pi)^i}{(2i + 1)!}.$
     4    $\displaystyle\sum_{i=0}^{\infty} \frac{(-1)^{i-1}}{i}(x - 1)^i.$

5   Consider the sequence of functions defined by

$$f_n(x) = \begin{cases} 0, & |x| \geq 1/n \\ nx + 1, & -1/n < x \leq 0 \\ -nx + 1, & 0 < x < 1/n. \end{cases}$$

(a) Let

$$\phi(x) = \begin{cases} 0, & x \neq 0 \\ 1, & x = 0. \end{cases}$$

(b) Does f converge to ϕ uniformly over $[-1, 1]$? [Hint: Is ϕ continuous relative to $[-1, 1]$?]

(c) Prove that if $0 \notin [a, b]$, then f converges to ϕ uniformly over $[a, b]$.

6   Use the Weierstrass M-Test to prove that $\sum_{i=0}^{\infty} x^i/i\,!$ is uniformly convergent over $[-r, r]$ for every $r > 0$.

Differentiation and Integration of Power Series

The sum function of a power series is continuous relative to the interior of its domain of convergence.

227 THEOREM

If $\sum_{i=0}^{\infty} c_i(x - a)^i$ is convergent for $|x - a| < r, r > 0$, and if

$$\phi(x) = \sum_{i=0}^{\infty} c_i(x - a)^i,$$

then ϕ is continuous over $]a - r, a + r[$.

Proof

Let

$$f_n(x) = \sum_{i=0}^{n} c_i(x - a)^i, \qquad n \in \mathbf{N}.$$

Each f_n is then a polynomial and hence is continuous everywhere.

Let x be any point in $]a - r, a + r[$. Then $0 \leq |x - a| < r$, so there exists a real number $r_1 > 0$ such that

$$|x - a| < r_1 < r.$$

Then the series $\sum_{i=0}^{\infty} c_i(x - a)^i$ is uniformly convergent over $[a - r_1, a + r_1]$, and since the f_n's are continuous relative to $[a - r_1, a + r_1]$, it follows from Theorem 223 that ϕ is continuous relative to $[a - r_1, a + r_1]$. Since $x \in [a - r_1, a + r_1]$, ϕ is continuous at x. Therefore ϕ is continuous over $]a - r, a + r[$. $\square$

The integral of a sum is the sum of the integrals, even in the infinite case of a power series.

228 THEOREM

If $\sum_{i=0}^{\infty} c_i(x - a)^i$ is convergent for $|x - a| < r, r > 0$, if

$$\phi(x) = \sum_{i=0}^{\infty} c_i(x - a)^i,$$

and if

$$a - r < x_1 < x_2 < a + r,$$

then

$$\phi \in \mathcal{R}[x_1, x_2],$$

and

$$\int_{x_1}^{x_2} \phi(x)\, dx = \sum_{i=0}^{\infty} c_i \int_{x_1}^{x_2} (x - a)^i\, dx.$$

Proof

That $\phi \in \mathcal{R}[x_1, x_2]$ follows easily from Theorem 227, since it can be shown using that theorem that ϕ is continuous over $[x_1, x_2]$.

Let $f_n(x) = \sum_{i=0}^{n} c_i(x - a)^i$. Then f_n converges uniformly to ϕ over $[x_1, x_2]$ (Theorem 226). Given $\varepsilon > 0$ choose n_0 so that

$$|\phi(x) - f_n(x)| < \frac{\varepsilon}{x_2 - x_1}$$

for all $x \in [x_1, x_2]$ and for all $n \geq n_0$. Then

$$\left| \int_{x_1}^{x_2} \phi(x)\, dx - \int_{x_1}^{x_2} f_n(x)\, dx \right| = \left| \int_{x_1}^{x_2} (\phi(x) - f_n(x))\, dx \right|$$

$$= |[\phi(x_n) - f_n(x_n)](x_2 - x_1)|, \qquad x_n \in [x_1, x_2]$$

$$= |\phi(x_n) - f_n(x_n)|\, |x_2 - x_1|$$

$$< \frac{\varepsilon}{x^2 - x_1} \cdot (x_2 - x_1) = \varepsilon$$

for all $n \geq n_0$, where x_n is the point in $[x_1, x_2]$ whose existence is guaranteed by the mean value theorem for integrals. Therefore

$$\int_{x_1}^{x_2} \phi(x)\, dx = \lim \left(\int_{x_1}^{x_2} f_n(x)\, dx \right)$$

$$= \lim \left[\int_{x_1}^{x_2} \left(\sum_{i=1}^{n} c^i(x - a)^i \right) dx \right]$$

$$= \lim \left[\sum_{i=1}^{n} \left(\int_{x_1}^{x_2} c_i(x - a)^i\, dx \right) \right]$$

$$= \lim \sum_{i=1}^{n} c_i \int_{x_1}^{x_2} (x - a)^i\, dx$$

$$= \sum_{i=1}^{\infty} c_i \int_{x_1}^{x_2} (x - a)^i\, dx. \quad \square$$

The derivative of the sum function of a power series can be obtained by differentiating the series term by term.

229 THEOREM

If $\sum_{i=0}^{\infty} c_i(x - a)^i$ is convergent for $|x - a| < r, r > 0$, and if

$$\phi(x) = \sum_{i=0}^{\infty} c_i(x - a)^i,$$

then ϕ is differentiable over $]a - r, a + r[$, and

$$\phi'(x) = \sum_{i=1}^{\infty} ic_i(x - a)^{i-1}$$

for every x in $]a - r, a + r[$.

Proof

Assume for the moment that $\sum_{i=1}^{\infty} ic_i(x - a)^{i-1}$ is convergent over $]a - r, a + r[$, and let

$$g(x) = \sum_{i=1}^{\infty} ic_i(x - a)^{i-1}.$$

Then, by Theorem 228,

$$\int_a^x g(t)\, dt = \sum_{i=1}^{\infty} ic_i \int_a^x (t - a)^{i-1}\, dt$$

$$= \sum_{i=1}^{\infty} c_i(x - a)^i \qquad \text{for every} \quad x \in]a - r, a + r[.$$

Therefore

$$\int_a^x g(t)\, dt = \phi(x) - c_0 \qquad \text{for every} \quad x \in]a - r, a + r[\ .$$

It follows that

$$\phi'(x) = g(x) \qquad \text{for every} \quad x \in]a - r, a + r[.$$

In order to complete the proof, we must show that $\sum_{i=1}^{\infty} ic_i(x - a)^{i-1}$ is, in fact, convergent for all x in $]a - r, a + r[$.

[1] Assume that $\sum_{i=1}^{\infty} ic_i(x_0 - a)^{i-1}$ converges absolutely for some real number x_0. Then

$$\sum_{i=1}^{\infty} ic_i(x_0 - a)^i = (x_0 - a) \sum_{i=1}^{\infty} ic_i(x_0 - a)^{i-1}$$

also converges absolutely, and since $|c_i| |x_0 - a|^i \le i|c_i| |x_0 - a|^i$ for every $i \in \mathbf{N}$, it follows that $\sum_{i=0}^{\infty} c_i(x_0 - a)^i$ converges absolutely. Hence absolute convergence of $\sum_{i=1}^{\infty} ic_i(x - a)^{i-1}$ implies absolute convergence of $\sum_{i=0}^{\infty} c_i(x - a)^i$.

[2] Now assume $\sum_{i=0}^{\infty} c_i(x_0 - a)^i$ converges absolutely for some $x_0 \neq a$. Let $\beta = |x_0 - a|$. If x is any real number with $|x - a| = \alpha$, where $0 < \alpha < \beta$, then $\sum_{i=1}^{\infty} i(\alpha/\beta)^i$ is convergent, since

$$\frac{(n+1)(\alpha/\beta)^{n+1}}{n(\alpha/\beta)^n} = \frac{n+1}{n}\left(\frac{\alpha}{\beta}\right),$$

and

$$\lim \frac{n+1}{n}\left(\frac{\alpha}{\beta}\right) = \left(\frac{\alpha}{\beta}\right) < 1.$$

Therefore, by Theorem 204,

$$\lim i\left(\frac{\alpha}{\beta}\right)^i = 0.$$

Therefore

$$\lim \frac{i|c_i|\alpha^i}{|c_i|\beta^i} = 0$$

and so there exists $n_0 \in \mathbf{N}$ such that

$$\frac{i|c_i|\alpha^i}{|c_i|\beta^i} < 1 \qquad \text{for all} \quad i \geq n_0.$$

Therefore

$$i|c_i|\alpha^i < |c_i|\beta^i \qquad \text{for all} \quad i \geq n_0.$$

But $\sum_{i=1}^{\infty} |c_i| \beta^i$ is convergent, since $\sum_{i=0}^{\infty} c_i(x_0 - a)^i$ converges absolutely and $|x_0 - a| = \beta$. Then, by the comparison test,

$$\sum_{i=1}^{\infty} i|c_i|\alpha^i = \alpha \sum_{i=1}^{\infty} i|c_i|\alpha^{i-1}$$

converges. Hence $\sum_{i=1}^{\infty} i|c_i|\alpha^{i-1}$ converges, and so $\sum_{i=1}^{\infty} ic_i(x - a)^{i-1}$ converges absolutely. Therefore, absolute convergence of $\sum_{i=0}^{\infty} c_i(x - a)^i$ for $x = x_0 \neq a$ implies absolute convergence of $\sum_{i=1}^{\infty} ic_i(x - a)^{i-1}$ for every x with $0 < |x - a| < |x_0 - a|$.

Paragraph [1] asserts that the domain of absolute convergence of

$$\sum_{i=1}^{\infty} ic_i(x - a)^{i-1}$$

is a subset of the domain of absolute convergence of $\sum_{i=1}^{\infty} c_i(x - a)^i$. That is, the radius of convergence of the former is no greater than that of the latter, since the only possible points at which a convergent power series is not absolutely convergent are the endpoints of its domain of convergence. On the other hand, paragraph [2] asserts that the radius of convergence of the former is at least as great as that of the latter. Therefore the two series have the same radius of convergence, so that if one of them converges for $|x - a| < r$, so does the other. $\square$

What can be done once to a power series can be done again, since the result of doing it once is another power series. The proof is to be done as an exercise.

230 COROLLARY

If $\sum_{i=0}^{\infty} c_i(x - a)^i$ is convergent for $|x - a| < r, r > 0$, and if

$$\phi(x) = \sum_{i=0}^{\infty} c_i(x - a)^i,$$

then $\phi^{(j)}(x)$ exists for every $x \in]a - r, a + r[$ and for every $j \in \mathbf{N}$. Furthermore,

$$\phi^{(j)}(x) = \sum_{i=j}^{\infty} i(i - 1) \cdots (i - j + 1)c_i(x - a)^{i-j}$$

for every $x \in]a - r, a + r[, j \in \mathbf{N}.\dagger$

Finally, we note that the coefficients in a power series can be expressed in terms of the derivatives of its sum function. The proof is to be done as an exercise.

231 COROLLARY

If $\sum_{i=0}^{\infty} c_i(x - a)^i$ is convergent for $|x - a| < r, r > 0$, and if

$$\phi(x) = \sum_{i=0}^{\infty} c_i(x - a)^i,$$

then

$$c_0 = \phi(a),$$

and

$$c_i = \frac{\phi^{(i)}(a)}{i!}, \qquad i \in \mathbf{N}.$$

$\dagger \phi^{(1)}(x) = \dfrac{d\phi}{dx}, \phi^{(i+1)}(x) = \dfrac{d\phi^{(i)}}{dx}, i \in \mathbf{N}.$

EXERCISES

1   Prove Corollary 230.

2   Prove Corollary 231.

3   Let

$$\phi(x) = 1 + \sum_{i=1}^{\infty} \frac{x^i}{i!}.$$

Prove that $\phi^{(j)}(x) = \phi(x)$ for every $x \in \mathbf{K}$ and for every $j \in \mathbf{N}$.

4   Let $\phi(x)$ be defined as in Exercise 3. Calculate the value of $\int_0^1 \phi(x)\, dx$ correct to four decimal places.

Taylor Series

Corollary 231 raises the following interesting question. Suppose that ϕ is a function defined over $]a - r, a + r[, r > 0$, and assume that $\phi^{(i)}(a)$ exists for every $i \in \mathbf{N}$. Assume, moreover, that the series

$$\phi(a) + \sum_{i=1}^{\infty} \frac{\phi^{(i)}(a)}{i!}(x - a)^i$$

converges for all $x \in]a - r, a + r[$. The question then is, does the equation

$$\phi(x) = \phi(a) + \sum_{i=1}^{\infty} \frac{\phi^{(i)}(a)}{i!}(x - a)^i$$

hold for every $x \in]a - r, a + r[$? A moment's reflection leads one to the answer "no, not necessarily," because if

$$\psi(x) = \begin{cases} \phi(x), & |x - a| < \tfrac{1}{2}r \\ \phi(x) + 1, & \tfrac{1}{2}r \le |x - a| < r \end{cases}$$

then

$$\psi(a) + \sum_{i=1}^{\infty} \frac{\psi^{(i)}(a)}{i!}(x - a)^i = \phi(a) + \sum_{i=1}^{\infty} \frac{\phi^{(i)}(a)}{i!}(x - a)^i$$

for every $x \in]a - r, a + r[$, but it is *not* the case that $\phi(x)$ and $\psi(x)$ are the same for every $x \in]a - r, a + r[$.

The remainder of the section will be devoted to a discussion of the circumstances under which the series

$$\phi(a) + \sum_{i=1}^{\infty} \frac{\phi^{(i)}(a)}{i!}(x - a)^i$$

actually *does* converge to $\phi(x)$. Our first step is to introduce a name for this series.

232 DEFINITION

Let ϕ be a function having the property that $\phi^{(i)}(a)$ exists for every $i \in \mathbf{N}$. The infinite series

$$\phi(a) + \sum_{i=1}^{\infty} \frac{\phi^{(i)}(a)}{i!}(x - a)^i$$

is called the *Taylor series of ϕ at a*. The Taylor series of ϕ at 0 is usually called the *Maclaurin series of ϕ*.

We can now restate Corollary 231 as follows:

233 COROLLARY

If $\sum_{i=0}^{\infty} c_i(x - a)^i$ converges for $|x - a| < r, r > 0$, then $\sum_{i=0}^{\infty} c_i(x - a)^i$ is the Taylor series at a of its sum function.

The coefficients of a convergent power series are uniquely determined by its sum function.

234 THEOREM   Uniqueness Theorem

If $\sum_{i=0}^{\infty} c_i(x - a)^i$ and $\sum_{i=0}^{\infty} d_i(x - a)^i$ both converge for $|x - a| < r$, $r > 0$, and if

$$\sum_{i=0}^{\infty} c_i(x - a)^i = \sum_{i=0}^{\infty} d_i(x - a)^i$$

for all x with $|x - a| < r$, then

$$c_i = d_i \qquad \text{for every} \quad i \in \mathbf{N} \cup \{0\}.$$

Proof

Let

$$\phi(x) = \sum_{i=0}^{\infty} c_i(x - a)^i, \qquad |x - a| < r.$$

It then follows from Corollary 231 that

$$c_0 = \phi(a), \qquad c_i = \frac{\phi^{(i)}(a)}{i!}, \qquad i \in \mathbf{N}.$$

But, since

$$\sum_{i=0}^{\infty} c_i(x - a)^i = \sum_{i=0}^{\infty} d_i(x - a)^i$$

for every x with $|x - a| < r$, we have

$$\phi(x) = \sum_{i=0}^{\infty} d_i(x - a)^i, \qquad |x - a| < r.$$

Therefore we may apply Corollary 231 again to obtain

$$d_0 = \phi(a) \qquad \text{and} \qquad d_i = \frac{\phi^{(i)}(a)}{i!}, \qquad i \in \mathbf{N}.$$

Hence

$$c_i = d_i \qquad \text{for every } i \in \mathbf{N} \cup \{0\}. \quad \square$$

Our next theorem provides a necessary and sufficient condition that the Taylor series of a given function converge to that function.

---

235 THEOREM   Taylor's Formula

Let $\phi, \phi', \ldots, \phi^{(n)}$ be continuous over $]a - r, a + r[$ for some $r > 0$ and for some $n \in \mathbf{N}$, and let $\phi^{(n+1)}(x)$ exist for every $x \in]a - r, a + r[$. If $x \in]a - r, a + r[$ and $x \neq a$, then there exists x_n with $a < x_n < x$ (if $x > a$) or $x < x_n < a$ (if $x < a$) such that

$$\phi(x) = \phi(a) + \frac{\phi'(a)}{1!}(x - a) + \cdots + \frac{\phi^{(n)}(a)}{n!}(x - a)^n$$

$$+ \frac{\phi^{(n+1)}(x_n)}{(n + 1)!}(x - a)^{n+1}.$$

Proof

Let $x \in]a - r, a + r[$ and assume that $x \neq a$. Then $(x - a)^{n+1} \neq 0$. Let

$$P_n(x) = \phi(a) + \frac{\phi'(a)}{1!}(x - a) + \cdots + \frac{\phi^{(n)}(a)}{n!}(x - a)^n,$$

and let

$$Q = \frac{[\phi(x) - P_n(x)](n + 1)!}{(x - a)^{n+1}}.$$

Then

$$\phi(x) = P_n(x) + \frac{(x - a)^{n+1}}{(n + 1)!}Q.$$

We shall now show that

$$Q = \phi^{(n+1)}(x_n)$$

for some x_n between a and x.

Let F_x be the function defined by

$$F_x(z) = -\phi(x) + \phi(z) + \phi'(z)(x - z)$$

$$+ \cdots + \frac{\phi^{(n)}(z)}{n!}(x - z)^n + \frac{(x - z)^{n+1}}{(n + 1)!}Q.$$

Note that $F_x(x) = 0$ and that

$$F_x(a) = -\phi(x) + P_n(x) + \frac{(x - a)^{n+1}}{(n + 1)!}Q$$

$$= -\phi(x) + P_n(x) + \phi(x) - P_n(x)$$

$$= 0.$$

Furthermore, F_x is continuous and differentiable at each z with $a \le z \le x$ (or $x \le z \le a$). Therefore, by Rolle's theorem, there exists x_n between a and x such that

$$F_x'(x_n) = 0.$$

But a simple calculation shows that

$$F_x'(z) = \frac{(x - z)^n}{n!}[\phi^{(n+1)}(z) - Q].$$

Therefore

$$\frac{(x - x_n)^n}{n!}[\phi^{(n+1)}(x_n) - Q] = 0,$$

and so, since $x_n \ne x$, we have

$$\phi^{(n+1)}(x_n) = Q. \quad \square$$

236 COROLLARY

Let ϕ and $\phi^{(i)}$ for every $i \in \mathbf{N}$ be continuous over $]a - r, a + r[$ for some $r > 0$, and for each $n \in \mathbf{N}$ and each $x \in]a - r, a + r[$ with $x \ne a$

let

$$R_n(x) = \frac{\phi^{(n+1)}(x_n)}{(n+1)!}(x-a)^{n+1},$$

where x_n is the point between a and x whose existence is guaranteed by Theorem 235. Then the Taylor series of ϕ at a converges to $\phi(x)$ for a given x with $0 < |x - a| < r$ if and only if

$$\lim R_n(x) = 0.$$

(The proof is to be done as an exercise.)

As an example, consider $\phi(x) = \sin x$. We have

$$\phi(x) = \sin x, \ \phi(0) = 0$$

$$\phi'(x) = \cos x, \ \phi'(0) = 1$$

$$\phi''(x) = -\sin x, \ \phi''(0) = 0$$

$$\phi'''(x) = -\cos x, \ \phi'''(0) = -1,$$

$$\phi^{(iv)}(x) = \sin x, \ \phi^{(iv)}(0) = 0.$$

Therefore the Maclaurin series of ϕ is

$$x - \frac{x^3}{3!} + \frac{x^5}{5!} - \frac{x^7}{7!} + \cdots = \sum_{i=1}^{\infty} (-1)^{i+1} \frac{x^{2i-1}}{(2i-1)!}.$$

Note that $\phi^{(n+1)}(x)$ is either $\pm \sin x$ or $\pm \cos x$, so that $|\phi^{(n+1)}(x)| \leq 1$ for every x. Hence

$$|R_n(x)| = \left| \frac{\phi^{(n+1)}(x_n)(x-a)^{n+1}}{(n+1)!} \right| \leq \frac{|x-a|^{n+1}}{(n+1)!}.$$

But the ratio test shows that

$$\sum_{n=1}^{\infty} \frac{(x-a)^{n+1}}{(n+1)!}$$

converges absolutely for every $x \in \mathbf{K}$, and so (Theorem 204)

$$\lim \frac{|x-a|^{n+1}}{(n+1)!} = 0$$

for every $x \in \mathbf{K}$. Therefore $\lim R_n(x) = 0$ for every $x \in \mathbf{K}$, and so the Maclaurin series of $\sin x$ converges to $\sin x$ for every $x \in \mathbf{K}$.

As a second example, consider $\phi(x) = \ln x$, $a = 1$ ("ln" denotes the natural logarithmic function). For this function we have

$$\phi(x) = \ln x, \qquad \phi(1) = 0,$$

$$\phi^{(i)}(x) = \frac{(-1)^{i+1}(i-1)!}{x^i},$$

$$\phi^{(i)}(1) = (-1)^{i+1}(i-1)!, \qquad i \in \mathbf{N}.$$

Therefore the Taylor series of $\ln x$ at 1 is

$$\sum_{i=1}^{\infty} \frac{(-1)^{i+1}(i-1)!}{i!}(x-1)^i = \sum_{i=1}^{\infty} \frac{(+1)^{i+1}}{i}(x-1)^i.$$

Furthermore,

$$R_n(x) = \frac{\phi^{(n+1)}(x_n)}{(n+1)!}(x-1)^{n+1}$$

$$= \frac{(-1)^n}{n+1}\left(\frac{x-1}{x_n}\right)^{n+1}$$

where x_n is between 1 and x.

If $1 < x \leq 2$, then

$$1 < x_n < x \leq 2,$$

and so

$$0 < (x-1) \leq 1 < x_n.$$

Therefore

$$0 < \frac{x-1}{x_n} < 1.$$

from which it follows that

$$\left| (-1)^n \left(\frac{x-1}{x_n}\right)^{n+1} \right| < 1$$

for all $x \in\ ]1, 2[$ and for every $n \in \mathbf{N}$.

If $\frac{1}{2} \leq x < x_n < 1$, then

$$1 - x \leq 1 - \tfrac{1}{2} = \tfrac{1}{2}.$$

Therefore

$$\frac{1-x}{x_n} \leq \frac{\tfrac{1}{2}}{x_n} < \frac{\tfrac{1}{2}}{\tfrac{1}{2}} = 1,$$

and we then have

$$\left| (-1)^n \left(\frac{x-1}{x_n} \right)^{n+1} \right| < 1$$

for all $x \in [\frac{1}{2}, 1[$ and for every $n \in \mathbf{N}$.

Combining these results, it follows that

$$|R_n(x)| < \frac{1}{n+1}$$

for every $x \in [\frac{1}{2}, 1[\cup]1, 2]$, and for every $n \in \mathbf{N}$. Therefore

$$\lim R_n(x) = 0$$

for every $x[\frac{1}{2}, 1[\cup]1, 2]$. Finally, then,

$$\sum_{i=1}^{\infty} \frac{(-1)^{i+1}}{i} (x-1)^i = \ln x$$

for every $x \in [\frac{1}{2}, 2]$.

As a matter of fact, the Taylor series of $\ln x$ at 1 converges to $\ln x$ for every $x \in]0, 2]$. The proof of this fact requires a different form for $R_n(x)$ than the one we have available, and so it will not be given here. Note that it is quite easy to establish (using the ratio test) that the series is convergent for every $x \in]0, 2]$; this fact in itself tells us nothing about the sum function, however.

EXERCISES

1   Prove that if $\sum_{i=0}^{\infty} c_i(x-a)^i$ converges for $|x-a| < r, r > 0$, and if $\sum_{i=0}^{\infty} c_i(x-a)^i = 0$ for every x with $|x-a| < r$, then $c_i = 0$ for every $i \in \mathbf{N}$.

2   Find the Taylor series of
(a) e^x at 0.
(b) e^x at 1.
(c) $\cos x$ at 0.
(d) $\cos x$ at $\pi/2$.
(e) $1/x$ at 1.

3   Prove that the Maclaurin series of $\cos x$ converges to $\cos x$ for every $x \in \mathbf{K}$.

4   Prove that the Maclaurin series of e^x converges to e^x for every $x \in \mathbf{K}$.

5   Prove Corollary 236.

6   Let ϕ be a polynomial function. Prove that for every $a \in \mathbf{K}$, the Taylor series of ϕ at a converges to $\phi(x)$ for every $x \in \mathbf{K}$.

7   Show that the mean value theorem for derivatives is a special case of Theorem 235.

APPENDIX

Sets, Relations, and Mappings

S_1 A *set* is a well-defined collection of objects called *members* of the set; by "well-defined" we mean that it is always possible to determine whether a given object is or is not a member of the collection.

Sets are generally denoted by capital letters, their members by lower case letters, and set membership by the symbol $\in$. Thus "$s \in S$" is read "s is a member of S," while "$t \notin S$" is read "t is not a member of S."

Sets can be defined by means of the *roster* notation, in which a list of all the members is enclosed by braces (for example, $\{1, 2, 3\}$), or by the *set-builder* $\{ \ : \ \}$, by means of which $\{x : x$ has property $P\}$ designates the set of all those objects which have property P.

S_2 Two sets are *equal* iff they have the same members. Thus $A = B$ if and only if $x \in A$ implies $x \in B$, and $x \in B$ implies $x \in A$.

S_3 A set A is said to be a *subset* of a set B, denoted by $A \subset B$, iff $x \in A$ implies $x \in B$. A set A is said to be a *proper* subset of set B iff $A \subset B$ and $A \neq B$.

201

S_4 The set having no members at all is called the *empty set* and is denoted by $\varnothing$.

S_5 If A and B are sets, then the *union* of A and B, denoted by $A \cup B$, is defined by

$$A \cup B = \{x : x \in A \quad \text{or} \quad x \in B\}.$$

The *intersection* of A and B, $A \cap B$, is defined by

$$A \cap B = \{x : x \in A \quad \text{and} \quad x \in B\}.$$

Set union and intersection are commutative, associative, and each is distributive over the other.

S_6 If A and B are sets, then the *difference* of A and B, denoted by $A - B$, is defined by

$$A - B = \{x : x \in A \quad \text{and} \quad x \notin B\}.$$

The set $A - B$ is also called the *complement* of B in A and is sometimes denoted by $C_A(B)$.

S_7 If $\mathscr{C}$ is any collection of sets, then

$$\cup\{M : M \in \mathscr{C}\} = \{x : x \in M \quad \text{for at least one } M \in \mathscr{C}\},$$

and

$$\cap\{M : M \in \mathscr{C}\} = \{x : x \in M \quad \text{for every} \quad M \in \mathscr{C}\}.$$

S_8 The *solution set* of an equation or inequation in n is the set of all those replacements for n which render the equation or inequation a true statement.

S_9 An *ordered pair* is any set of the form $\{\{a, b\}, \{a\}\}$; the usual notation for such an ordered pair is (a, b). Two ordered pairs (a, b) and (c, d) are *equal* if and only if $a = c$ and $b = d$.

S_{10} The *cartesian product* of two sets A and B, denoted by $A \times B$, is defined by

$$A \times B = \{(a, b) : a \in A \quad \text{and} \quad b \in B\}.$$

S_{11} A *relation* from set A to set B is a subset of $A \times B$ (that is, every relation from A to B is a subset of $A \times B$, and every subset of $A \times B$ is a relation from A to B). If ρ is a relation from A to B, we write $a\rho b$ iff $(a, b) \in \rho$.

S_{12} An *equivalence relation* on a set A is a relation ρ from A to A such that

[1] $a\rho a$ for every $a \in A$,

[2] $a\rho b$ implies $b\rho a$,

and

[3] $a\rho b$ and $b\rho c$ imply $a\rho c$.

S_{13} If ρ is an equivalence relation on set A and $a \in A$, then $[a]$ denotes the set

$$\{x \in A : x\rho a\};$$

$[a]$ is called the *ρ-equivalence class* containing a. Equivalence classes have the following properties:

[1] $a\rho b$ implies $[a] = [b]$.

[2] $a\rlap{\,/}{\rho}b$ (i.e. $(a, b) \notin \rho$) implies $[a] \cap [b] = \varnothing$.

[3] $\cup \{[a] : a \in A\} = A$.

S_{14} A *mapping f* from set X to set Y is a relation from X to Y having the property that

$$(x_1, y_1) \in f \quad \text{and} \quad (x_1, y_2) \in f \quad \text{implies} \quad y_1 = y_2.$$

The *domain* of a mapping f from X to Y is

$$\{x \in X : \text{there exists } y \in Y \text{ such that } (x, y) \in f\}.$$

For each x in the domain of a mapping f of X into Y, $f(x)$ denotes the unique $y \in Y$ such that $(x, y) \in f$. Thus

$$y = f(x) \quad \text{if and only if} \quad (x, y) \in f.$$

S_{15} A mapping *of* set X *into* set Y is a mapping from X into Y whose domain is X.

S_{16} A mapping f of X into Y is said to be *one-to-one* iff

$$(x_1, y_1) \in f \quad \text{and} \quad (x_2, y_1) \in f \quad \text{imply} \quad x_1 = x_2.$$

S_{17} A mapping f of X into Y is said to be *onto* Y iff for every $y \in Y$ there exists an $x \in X$ such that $(x, y) \in f$.

S_{18} A *binary operation* on a set S is a mapping of $S \times S$ into S.

S_{19} Let S be a set upon which are defined a binary operation $*$ and an equivalence relation ρ. A binary operation $\circ$ defined on the ρ-equivalence classes of S by means of the equation

$$[x] \circ [y] = [x * y]$$

is said to be *well-defined* iff $x\rho p$ and $y\rho q$ imply $(x * y)\rho(p * q)$.

Algebra

A_1 A *group* $(G; *)$ is a nonempty set G upon which a binary operation $*$ is defined such that

[1] $(a * b) * c = a * (b * c)$ for all a, b, and c in G,

[2] there exists $e \in G$ such that $a * e = e * a = a$ for every $a \in G$, and

[3] for each $a \in G$ there exists $a^{-1} \in G$ such that $a * a^{-1} = a^{-1} * a = e$. The element e is called the *identity* of $(G; *)$, and a^{-1} is called the *inverse* of a.

A_2 An *abelian group* $(G; *)$ is a group such that

$$a * b = b * a \qquad \text{for every} \quad a \in G.$$

A_3 The following hold in every group $(G; *)$:

[1] $a * b = a * c$ implies $b = c$.

[2] $a * b = c * b$ implies $a = c$.

[3] $(a^{-1})^{-1} = a$ for every $a \in G$.

[4] For each $a \in G$ and each $b \in G$ there exists a unique $x \in G$ such that $a * x = b$, and there exists a unique $y \in G$ such that $y * a = b$.

A_4 An *integral domain* $(D; +, \cdot)$ is a nonempty set D upon which are defined two binary operations $+$ and $\cdot$ such that:

[1] $(D; +)$ is an abelian group with identity 0,

[2] $a \cdot b = b \cdot a$ for all a and b in D,

[3] $(a \cdot b) \cdot c = a \cdot (b \cdot c)$ for all a, b, and c in D,

[4] $a \cdot (b + c) = a \cdot b + a \cdot c$ for all a, b, and c in D,

[5] there exists $1 \in D$, $1 \neq 0$, such that

$$a \cdot 1 = 1 \cdot a = a \qquad \text{for every} \quad a \in D,$$

and

[6] $a \cdot b = 0$, $a \in D$, and $b \in D$ imply either

$$a = 0 \text{ or } b = 0.$$

The inverse of a relative to the abelian group $(D; +)$ is usually denoted by $-a$.

A_5 The following hold in every integral domain $(D; +, \cdot)$:

[1] $a + c = b + c$ implies $a = b$.

[2] $-(-a) = a$ for every $a \in D$.

[3] $a \cdot 0 = 0$ for every $a \in D$.

[4] $a(-b) = (-a)b = -ab$ for all a and b in D.

[5] $(-a)(-b) = ab$ for all a and b in D.

[6] $ab = ac$ and $a \neq 0$ imply $b = c$.

A_6 *Subtraction* can be defined in any integral domain by means of the equation

$$a - b = a + (-b).$$

The following then hold in any integral domain $(D; +, \cdot)$:

[1] $-(a + b) = -a - b$ for all a and b in D.

[2] $-(a - b) = -a + b$ for all a and b in D.

[3] $(a - b) - c = a - (b + c)$ for all a, b, and c in D.

[4] $a(b - c) = ab - ac$ for all a, b, and c in D.

A_7 An *ordered* integral domain $(D; +, \cdot; P)$ is an integral domain $(D; +, \cdot)$ together with a subset P of D such that:

[1] $a \in P$ and $b \in P$ imply $(a + b) \in P$,

[2] $a \in P$ and $b \in P$ imply $ab \in P$,

and

[3] for each $a \in D$ exactly one of the following holds:

$$a \in P, \qquad a = 0, \qquad -a \in P.$$

A_8 In an ordered integral domain $(D; +, \cdot; P)$ the relation $>$ is defined by

$$a > b \qquad \text{iff} \qquad (a - b) \in P,$$

and the relation $<$ is defined by

$$a < b \qquad \text{iff} \qquad b > a.$$

The following then hold in every ordered integral domain $(D; +, \cdot; P)$:

[1] $a > b$ implies $a + c > b + c$ for every $c \in D$.

[2] $a > b$ and $c > 0$ implies $ac > bc$.

[3] $a > b$ and $c < 0$ implies $ac < bc$.

[4] $a > b$ and $b > c$ imply $a > c$.

[5] $a \neq 0$ implies $a^2 > 0$.

A_9 In an ordered integral domain $(D; +, \cdot, P)$, the notion of *absolute value* can be defined as follows:

$$|a| = \begin{cases} a & \text{if } a \geq 0 \\ -a & \text{if } a < 0 \end{cases}$$

("$|a|$" is read "absolute value of a."). The following then hold in every ordered integral domain $(D; +, \cdot; P)$:

[1] $|a| \geq 0$ for every $a \in D$.

[2] $|ab| = |a|\,|b|$ for all a and b in D.

[3] $|a + b| \leq |a| + |b|$ for all a and b in D.

A_{10} A *field* $(F; +, \cdot)$ is an integral domain having the additional property that for every $a \in F$ with $a \neq 0$ there exists $a^{-1} \in F$ such that $a \cdot a^{-1} = 1$ (that is, $(F - \{0\}; \cdot)$ is an abelian group).

A_{11} *Division* can be defined in any field $(F; +, \cdot)$ by means of the equation

$$\frac{a}{b} = a \cdot b^{-1}, b \neq 0.$$

The following then hold in every field $(F; +, \cdot)$:

[1] $\dfrac{a}{b} + \dfrac{c}{d} = \dfrac{ad + bc}{bd}, bd \neq 0.$

[2] $\dfrac{a}{b} \cdot \dfrac{c}{d} = \dfrac{ac}{bd}, bd \neq 0.$

[3] $\dfrac{a/b}{c/d} = \dfrac{ad}{bc}, bc \neq 0, d \neq 0.$

[4] $-\dfrac{a}{b} = \dfrac{-a}{b} = \dfrac{a}{-b}, b \neq 0.$

A_{12} We say that $(F; +, \cdot; P)$ is an *ordered field* iff $(F; +, \cdot)$ is a field and $(F; +, \cdot; P)$ is an ordered integral domain. In an ordered field,

$$\frac{a}{b} > 0 \qquad \text{if and only if} \quad ab > 0.$$

A_{13} Let S be a set upon which an order relation $<$ is defined, and let T be a set upon which an order relation $\ll$ is defined. A mapping α of S into T is said to be *order-preserving* iff

$$s_1 \text{ and } s_2 \text{ in } S \qquad \text{and} \qquad s_1 < s_2 \text{ imply } \alpha(s_1) \ll \alpha(s_2).$$

If an addition operation $+$ is defined on S, and if an addition operation $\oplus$ is defined on T, we say that a mapping α of S into T *preserves sums* iff

$$\alpha(s_1 + s_2) = \alpha(s_1) \oplus \alpha(s_2)$$

for every s_1 and s_2 in S.

Similarly, if multiplication operations $\cdot$ and $\odot$ are defined on S and T respectively, a mapping α of S into T preserves *products* iff

$$\alpha(s_1 \cdot s_2) = \alpha(s_1) \odot \alpha(s_2).$$

A_{14} Two algebraic systems are said to be *isomorphic* (or one is said to be a *copy* of the other) iff there exists a one-to-one mapping of one onto the other that preserves the operations of the systems.

Logic

There are two relatively sophisticated logical principles that are used frequently in this text. Since they are often used in conjunction with each other, and since a lack of understanding of them can produce serious difficulties, a brief explanation is included here.

L_1 The first principle is the Rule of Conditional Proof. This rule states that if the assumption that a formula P is true leads to the truth of a formula Q, then the formula "if P, then Q" is true. For example, to prove the formula

"If $A \subset B$, then $A \cup B = B$,"

we assume that $A \subset B$ and show that it then follows that $A \cup B = B$.

L_2 The second principle is the Rule of Universal Generalization. This rule states that if a formula P concerning x is true, then the formula

"For every x, P is true"

is also true, provided that the formula P contains no occurrences of x in phrases such as "there exists an x" or "for some x". In other words, as far as P is concerned, x is "fixed but arbitrary".

As an example involving both L_1 and L_2, consider the following proof of the formula

"If $A \subset B$, then $A \cup B \subset B$."

Statement	Reason
1. $A \subset B$.	1. Assumption
2. $x \in A \cup B$.	2. Assumption
3. $x \in A$ or $x \in B$.	3. Definition of union
4. If $x \in A$, then $x \in B$.	4. Line 1
5. $x \in B$.	5. Lines 3 and 4
6. If $x \in A \cup B$, then $x \in B$.	6. Lines 2 and 5, rule of conditional proof.
7. For every x, if $x \in A \cup B$, then $x \in B$.	7. Rule of universal generalization.
8. $A \cup B \subset B$.	8. Definition of $\subset$.
9. If $A \subset B$, then $A \cup B \subset B$.	9. Lines 1 and 8, rule of conditional proof.

References

Johnson, Richard E. *First Course in Abstract Algebra*. Englewood Cliffs, N.J.: Prentice-Hall, Inc., 1953.

Perlis, Sam. *Introduction to Algebra*. Waltham, Mass.: Blaisdell Publishing Co., 1966.

Stoll, Robert R. *Sets, Logic, and Axiomatic Theories*. San Francisco: W. H. Freeman and Co., 1961.

Suppes, Patrick. *Introduction to Logic*. Princeton, N.J.: Van Nostrand Co., Inc., 1957.

Index

211